A PICTORIAL HISTORY OF
TELEVISION

A PICTORIAL HISTORY OF
TELEVISION

by Irving Settel and William Laas

GROSSET & DUNLAP, INC.
A NATIONAL GENERAL COMPANY
Publishers   New York

Dedication:
To the ingenious and energetic men who created a miracle of communication. . . . with the hope that it will communicate inspiration to improve the world.

Contents

PICTURE CREDITS

Photographs, engravings, drawings and other illustrations in this book are used through the courtesy of the following organizations:

New York Public Library, American Museum of Natural History, Western Union Telegraph Company, New York Telephone Company, American Telephone and Telegraph Company, Radio Corporation of America, Television Age Magazine, Broadcasting Magazine, National Broadcasting Company, Westinghouse Corporation, National Educational Television, Columbia Broadcasting System, American Broadcasting Company, Bell Telephone Laboratories, General Electric Company, Allen B. DuMont Laboratories, WOR-Mutual Broadcasting System, Philco Corporation, Hartwest Productions, United States Navy, United States Army, Educasting Systems, Incorporated, Brown Brothers, Culver Company and Wide World Company.

Credits and thanks for many of the photographs go to the following individuals:

Trevor L. Christie, Edward Reynolds, Jane Hoffnagle, Richard Giacoloni, Art Selby, Walter I. Siegel, Thomas Cook Knight, Rosenfeld, F. A. Schultz, Aiklee, Harold Stein, Robert Perkins, Matthews, Eileen Darbl, Gary Wagner, Walt Davis, J. Peter Happel, Archie Lieberman, George Harris, Robert Philips, Vernon Merritt III, T. C. Rappoport, Bill Mitchell and Joseph G. Chenoweth.

Introduction

Television can be a controversial subject, but it is not our purpose here to enter the argument. In this book we neither pass judgment on nor attempt to predict the future of TV. We will let the medium tell its own fascinating story. In scarcely twenty years, a new kind of communication has wrought a cultural revolution, but it has done so in the guise of fun. All but the youngest readers will recall with nostalgia the great moments pictured here, whether "great" in the memorable sense or the notorious. We were there, with our eyes glued to the flickering tube. We saw it grow in size and in competence; we felt its influence, though hardly realizing what it was doing to us. Now we know. Let us see how it came about.

Of all the inventions that mark great eras in communications history, television must surely rank as the greatest since the written word. The telegraph, telephone, motion picture, radio, or for that matter the post office, each radically changed the way men live. Television is changing the way we *think*. It instantly transmits a replica of real events in lifelike motion, sound, and color. It is pure electronic magic, something strange in the world, and to thoughtful people rather frightening. Not since man first learned to put his ideas down in writing, thousands of years ago, has any new technique for transmitting ideas had such an impact on civilization.

These may sound like grandiose words for a staring glass eye in the living room that some call the "boob tube," particularly when soap operas and beer commercials flit across the fluorescent screen. Yet to label television revolutionary is no exaggeration. Marshall McLuhan, the Canadian philosopher of the TV era, says somewhat cryptically: "The medium is the message." In ways so subtle and yet profound that we are not yet sure of their implications, television not only conveys information, it creates it. An event occurs, a speech is delivered, a drama is staged. What actually happened can not be changed, the truth of it does not change, yet when seen on television, the "message" of the event does change, i.e., the effect on the recipient is different than if conveyed to him through any other medium.

Since the time of Moses and for centuries before him, civilized men have had the habit of adjusting their thinking to an orderly sequence of words. A logical conclusion—the message—emerges out of a series of mental steps. When we view television, most of the steps are skipped. Real life comes pouring effortlessly into our eyes, ears, and minds—or so it seems. The viewer-listener has no need to spell out or reason out the message. It is *there.* At least he is persuaded it is there, and he is right there with it, immersed in it. Because the image of an event is infinitely closer to reality than any written or spoken account, television has a way of becoming more real than life itself.

During the past few years, television has pungently demonstrated its revolutionary power in reporting three political assassinations and a war in Vietnam. The new medium added a dimension to national tragedy that unmistakably affected the national character. Reported in words, however vivid and shocking, grim events remain for most people in the abstract, as if happening far away to someone else. On television they come shrieking and moaning into the privacy of home; they hit us in the gut.

As a medium of entertainment, too, television alters our thought processes in a way that many find disturbing. When society parades its affluence and gaiety in half-hour segments all day long, the less privileged, be they frustrated college students as well as Negro or other elements of the poor, become restive. An accent on violence in TV drama has agitated sociologists and members of Congress. So has the public health aspect of cigarette TV advertising. In a later installment of his ruminations, McLuhan punned, "The medium is the *massage.*" A child born to TV's constant "massaging," to personal involvement either in fact or in fantasy via the electronic eye, will grow up with a different kind of mind than his word-trained father or grandfather.

Whether the consequences of this modern wizardry are for good or ill has been much debated. Television is hailed by educators for its potentialities, damned by critics for its shortcomings, scorned by the intelligentsia, swallowed whole by the larger segments of the population. One fact is clear: because of television's impact, the world will never be the same again. Our future has been set on a new course in every respect imaginable, in every social institution, custom, belief, or set of values. Some of these changes are already evident in show business, in sports, in political campaigns, in urban disorder. Some can only be guessed at, with the fear and trepidation that always accompany change, but perhaps with good cause for optimism as well. Judging by past history, improvements in communication have always been for the better of mankind, never for the worse. And television is the greatest improvement of all.

How it began

Much longer ago than most people suspect, this sometimes constructive, subversive, amusing, irritating, informative, ridiculous, noble, ignoble and always astonishing medium began as a gleam in an electronic tinkerer's eye. We say "astonishing" because when considered purely as technology, television is almost unbelievable. All earlier types of communication had severe limitations. Five hundred years since Gutenberg invented movable type, hugs masses of the world's population still can not read. The printed word does not communicate with *them*. Even radio is limited by language. In an historic example, the world did not fully understand Adolf Hitler until almost too late, partly because it did not hear his murderous radio diatribes delivered in the original German. In contrast, television knows no illiterates. Tiny children understand what they view on the home screen; even cats and dogs seem fascinated. Communication via TV is both instantaneous and *complete.* For the first time since Genesis, man has the power to reach deep into the senses of all his fellows, everywhere, with the speed of light.

When the word "television" first invaded our dictionaries, some linguists grumbled. It combines a Greek root (*tele,* far) with a Latin root (*video, videre,* I see) in a mismatch that offends the scholarly. But in truth, "far-I-see" in two languages is most appropriate. The word suggests a truly international science, derived not alone from ancient Greece and Rome but from all the descendant cultures in Europe and America.

Some years ago, Soviet propaganda provoked world mockery by claiming television to be a Russian invention. The fact is that a pre-revolutionary Russian, Boris Rosing, and an American of Russian origin, Vladimir Zworykin, did play important roles in

TV development—but so did scores of other men, spread over many countries and several millennia. The era of one-man, one-patent in this field ended with the nineteenth century. The telegraph may have had its Morse, the telephone its Bell, the wireless its Marconi, but even that is debatable. Isaac Newton once said: "If I have seen further, it is by standing on the shoulders of giants." And Albert Einstein: "My inner and outer life are based on the labors of other men, living and dead." Television is indeed built on the labor of giants. It is the fruit of at least a dozen separate lines of scientific and engineering research, converging in the twentieth century through the organized effort characteristic of our time. And it is still in its infancy.

What television does

Television is so sophisticated in concept that many of the people who make and repair TV sets don't fully understand how it works. Essentially, it is a controlled dance of electrons that accomplishes the following:

At the sending end, a TV camera points toward a scene and picks up an image of it, like a movie camera. However, instead of focusing this image on a film which is chemically sensitive to light, the TV camera focuses it on a material that is *electrically* sensitive to light. The photo-sensitive material conducts electricity in proportion to the intensity of the light striking it. By means of a scanning device, the image is broken up into tiny bits. The current induced by light from each bit in turn is transmitted as a separate impulse but in very rapid sequence. A dark bit of the image induces a weak current, a light bit a strong current, and a gray bit a medium current. The result is a continuous electrical "signal" from the photo-sensitive material that fluctuates in exact proportion to the darkness, lightness, or grayness of successive parts of the scene in front of the camera.

If the transmission is in color, the principle is the same except that light entering the camera is subdivided by filters into three component colors. Three signals are transmitted instead of one. Each signal fluctuates to match the amount of red, green, or blue light coming from the scene.

At the receiving end, your picture tube reverses the scanning process. In response to the incoming signal from each bit of the image in turn, it projects a beam of electrons against the corresponding area of the inner face of the tube. This is coated with a fluorescent material that glows brightly or weakly according to the intensity of the beam striking it. Since the beam fluctuates in tune with the signal, and the sigial in tune with the original scene, the tube's coating now also will glow in tune with the scene. It reproduces each part of the image in proper position and in the same sequence as transmitted. All this happens so swiftly that your eye combines all the little dark or light specks into a single picture. You are not aware of what is happening until something goes wrong with the set and you can see that it is merely tracing a series of horizontal lines.

In color sets, the principle is again the same except that the fluorescent materials in the tube's coating are of three kinds, called phosphors, that glow in three colors in accordance with the three signals transmitted.

Sounds simple? It isn't. We haven't even tried to describe *how* the picture is scanned electronically (with no moving, mechanical parts), which was the key invention in making television practical. To accomplish such a remarkable effect, brilliant men in many lands marshalled immense technical resources, and it took a long, long time. To trace the origin of television in scientific thought, we must go back to Aristotle. To find its true beginning as a goal in communications, we could go back to the era of the Neanderthal man.

The role of radio

For the sake of clarity and continuity, it is necessary first to dispel the notion that television is the recent child of radio. While this was true in a business sense—the great broadcasting empires built on audio moved naturally into video—television technically does not depend upon or stem from wireless transmission. Its concept actually preceded radio by more than half a century and its direct ancestor was the telegraph. One of your co-authors has reason to remember this well.

As a cub on the *New York World* in the late Twenties (when radio itself had scarcely emerged from the crystal-set stage), Bill Laas wrote a starry-eyed Sunday feature entitled "When Television Comes to Every Home." His article was based on promising experiments that had *already* tagged the transmitting of images as the real goal of broadcasting research. (The writer predicted it would take ten years, which if not for World War II would have been substantially correct.) In retrospect, voice radio was a compromise with the difficult problem of duplicating pictures, just as silent movies were a compromise with the real aim of duplicating live, spoken theater.

The film art did not attain maturity until sound could accompany sight; neither did the broadcasting art until sight was added to sound. The earlier products were each temporarily acceptable but incomplete, mere curtain raisers for the main show to come. If television hardware had been ready along with telephone hardware when wireless entered the scene, there might never have been any "blind" radio at all. Today there are strong indications that the future for television of superior quality may well lie in transmission via cable.

As a race we have lived so long with words that we easily forget they were, originally, a substitute for pictures. The story of television completes a full circle. Transmitting an *image* has been the instinctive aim of all communication arts since man first learned to speak. It has taken a super-sophisticated triumph of man's insatiable curiosity and ingenuity to restore the "message" of mankind to its most primitive form.

New York, Sept. 1969

Irving Settel
William Laas

A PICTORIAL HISTORY OF
TELEVISION

1. The Beginnings

Among the multitudes of living creatures that inhabited the primordial earth, man alone developed the faculty of communicating with other members of his race. Although, much to our astonishment, we have since discovered that porpoises and perhaps other animals "talk" in fairly precise signals, none but man was able to organize his speech into systematic thought, and his thoughts into the permanent form of conveyed information. It was precisely his ability to communicate that differentiated man from beast, that gave rise to human society, government, religion, industry, and finally to the sciences; that lifted mankind, for good or ill, to full command of the habitable universe. Intelligence without communication was not enough.

To illustrate, we know that an intelligent chimpanzee can learn to pile up some boxes so as to reach a banana dangling from the ceiling. He might teach the trick by imitation to another bright chimpanzee in the same room with him. But he cannot explain it to a chimp in *another* room (or at a later time). If faced with the same problem, each chimpanzee must start all over again to figure out the answer for himself—and only the most intelligent are capable of doing so. Primitive man alone was able to tell the next generation how to make a fire or track a mastodon. His children began learning where he left off. In this way—through communication—the entire tribe gradually acquired the knowledge of its brightest individuals, and so learned how to assure survival by mastering nature.

We refer to this unique human faculty as the power of speech, but in relevance to television, it will be observed that speech originally was a substitute for images. The sounds a man made with his voice were intended to suggest real things. A word like "hog" imitated the grunt of a pig, creating a mental *picture* of the object the speaker wanted to describe. When confronted with strangers of other tribes, a man reverted to sign language—he described pictures in the air with his hands or by dance movements of his body. When he wanted to make a record of his ideas, he scratched pictures into the soft stone walls of certain caves. Or he sculptured statues of what he had in mind, and some of these became idols.

Prehistoric cave paintings were one of man's first attempts to communicate with his fellows through art. Here is an image of a bull from the famous Lascaux caves of southwest France—judged to be from 15,000 to 20,000 years old.

Idols were among mankind's initial instruments to communicate with the gods and in some cases to strike terror in their enemies. This is an Hawaiian war idol.

An 1883 cartoonist's spoofing of the "impossible" idea of transmitting distant views by some kind of electrical apparatus.

The first writing was picture-writing, still visible to us in ancient Egyptian hieroglyphics or modern Chinese ideograms. In time, the pictures developed into symbols, that is, into formalized marks representing spoken words. Often the original meaning disappeared or the pictures acquired new meanings by association. The illustration on page 3 shows an example in Chinese: a picture of three women comes to mean "noisy." Centuries later the marks were broken down into alphabets, consisting of purely symbolic characters which could be freely combined to make new words. So was created highly precise writing as we know it in the Western world today. So also was created the art of thinking and speaking in a much more complex way than primitive man could develop with his simple grunts and picture-symbols.

The written word—the ability to freeze ideas into a form that could be transmitted over a distance or preserved in time—vastly accelerated civilized progress. Early peoples saw in The Word a kind of magic, and stood in awe of those who could read or write it. The Bible—which originally meant simply "The Book" —began as the recorded history of the Jews. But because it represented the accumulated wisdom of generations of great leaders, it became the Holy Bible, the prophetic word of God. In other religions, too, the possession of a book, a written record, came to distinguish advanced peoples from the illiterate, barbarian tribes.

Sign language and signalling were one method of communicating ideas in primitive societies. This 1873 engraving showed an American Plains Indian informing his tribe that a herd of buffalo is roaming nearby.

Ancient civilizations used pictures representing a word, an idea, or a sound instead of an alphabet. This Egyptian hieroglyphic inscription shows two ancient pharaohs making offering to their god, Amen-Ra.

Images vs. words

Once The Word existed, it was natural for the alert of mind to seek better methods of communicating verbal ideas to others. By communicating, the leaders could control larger areas of land and larger bodies of workers and troops. War drums and smoke signals, trumpets and bells, flags and banners, the swift couriers of Herodotus and of the Incas, semaphores, yodeling in the Swiss Alps . . . all were efforts to send specific information through time and space. The type of signal used was a convenience, not an end in itself. The end was a message in words. Men were never satisfied. They kept trying to improve the signal or message until it ap-

Chinese writing still in use today illustrates how pictures preceded words in the development of language. (1) is the Chinese ideogram for "woman." When (2) the woman has a roof over her head, she is at home, the Chinese idea of peace, and the character now means "tranquil." In (3) a cluster of three women without a roof to the Chinese suggests gossip; this ideogram means "noisy." With the invention of the alphabet, words became still further removed from the original images. Television reverses the process. It can convey the idea of "noisy" through images and sound without ever using the word, and viewers can understand TV without ever learning to speak, read, or write a language.

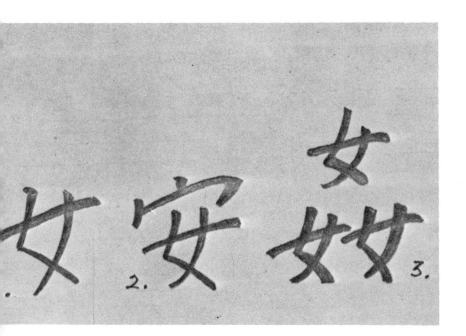

proached the real thing; or they tried to improve the method of communication until it approached the speed and reliability of direct human contact. In our own country, Benjamin Franklin's creation of the United States Postal Service may have been his greatest single contribution to unifying the divided colonies.

Over this long period, from prehistoric times to the eighteenth century, despite the dominance of The Word, the closest approach to reality continued to be an image. In the absence of pictures, poets used words to invoke them, in the much admired technique called imagery. Early civilizations are often remembered more vividly for their art than for their writing. Every religion acquired its altars, its icons, its replicas of the deity. Powerful rulers erected statues of themselves in heroic poses, clothed in godly raiment. In fact, a principal religious issue of ancient times was the rivalry between heathen idol worship and mystical ideas expressed in words.

The dance was another means of communication of ideas through bodily movements in ancient times. The modern moving image on TV inherits the tradition of this graceful Ionian dance.

When Moses went to Mount Sinai, the Israelites took advantage of his absence to worship the Golden Calf. When he came down from the mountain he bore a Commandment that said: "Thou shalt not make unto thee any graven image . . . Thou shalt not bow down thyself to them or serve them." Thousands of years later, confronted with idolatry among pagan Arab Bedouins, Mohammed wrote into the Koran a taboo on realistic images of any kind. Thus the prophet doomed Moslem art to a kind of decorative geometry. These great lawgivers sensed that a visual image could bypass the powers of verbal reason. It entered the mind through the eye, most perceptive of human organs, with a direct emotional appeal. Fearing the power of The Image over their unlettered followers, the holy men fought it. Later, as civilization advanced and The Word gained indisputed preeminence, they joined it.

In the fifteenth century, the Renaissance dispelled the Dark Ages of medieval Europe through a revival of ancient learning. Significantly, the greatest flowering of the Renaissance spirit took place in the arts, including painting and sculpture. Men like Leonardo da Vinci and Michelangelo broke loose from centuries of restraint, communicating their views of the world by depicting events as if happening before one's eyes. The Image, tamed, once again emerged to challenge The Word. But the invention of printing, in the same century, vastly accelerated the education of mankind in a verbal discipline.

Gutenberg and other early typographers created the literate world, the Age of Words. It is interesting to note, however, that previous manuscript books had always been heavily illuminated (illustrated by hand), and so was Gutenberg's printed Bible of 1456. In restrospect, his use of movable type for the text seems almost incidental to his purpose. Had Gutenberg known how to print pictures as informative as the words, he might have created an Age of Images. Several hundred years later, through technical progress in printing and engraving, many periodicals and books (such as this one) have again become heavily pictorial.

These reflections make it clear that from prehistoric times to the present, the tantalizing prospect of directly conveying images, not merely words that represent images, has been a challenge that has inspired man through the centuries. As soon as it could be done to some degree—in painting, for instance, or in photography and engraving—it was done.

The Greek philosopher Aristotle, developed a concept of atomic science in the third century B.C.

When the age of scientific thought arrived, the aim in communications became that of finding some technical means to transmit pictures over a distance. Because the task proved difficult in the extreme, it eluded dreamers for centuries. Yet the goal remained.

Television's family tree

Before television could be invented, that is, put together as a working tool, all sorts of seemingly unrelated advances first had to be achieved. In ancient Greece, Aristotle taught that matter is composed of invisible and, he thought, indivisible atoms. Since the Greeks had no experimental evidence, it was but a brilliant guess. Yet it fascinated scientific minds from that moment on. Aristotle supplied the philosophical basis for more than two thousand years of deduction, experiment, and discovery that led, in our own time, to harnessing the electrons of which atoms are composed, and so, far down the road, to modern television. To pick up the trail that leads directly to this marvelous manipulation of nature's mysterious forces, one must skip many centuries to the beginnings of electrical science.

The word "electricity" entered our language in 1600 in *De Magnete,* the major work of William Gilbert, of England. He was the first to make a distinction between magnetism, a natural force recognized since ancient times, and static electricity produced by rubbing certain materials such as wool or sulphur. In 1746, Professor Pieter van Musschenbroek of Leyden (now Leiden), Holland, accidentally discovered that electric energy could be built up like a head of water behind a dam. He had hooked up a glass bottle containing water to a source of weak static electricity. When the good professor's assistant grasped one of the wires from the bottle, he received a fearful shock. The forceful discharge from this "Leyden jar" was a scientific sensation. Benjamin Franklin pursued it with his famous experiment in 1752, proving that a lightning flash was of similar nature (and coming very close to electrocuting himself with the tremendous celestial voltage).

In 1800 Alessandro Volta's "pile," or battery, provided a means of controlling electricity by storing it for release at will. During the next thirty years men of various lands, including Volta in Italy, André Ampère in France, George Ohm in Germany, and Joseph Henry in America rounded out knowledge of the behavior of an electric current and gave it a mathematical basis. Their names are recalled in volts, amperes, ohms, and henries, all units of electrical measurement.

Next, the telegraph

Observation that an electrical discharge traveled, literally, at lightning speed led logically to the idea of using the mysterious new force to transmit messages. Franklin mused on this possibility. Centuries earlier a prophetic Englishman, Roger Bacon, had made the mistake (for his time) of foreseeing communication by electricity. He was imprisoned in 1267 for dealing in black magic. In the sixteenth century Giovanni Battista della Porta, a young Italian of fertile imagination, conceived of a "sympathetic telegraph" using "natural magic," by which he meant magnetism, to send signals.

One of Ampère's more far-out schemes was a set of twenty-six magnetic needles so rigged up that the needle deflections would signal the letters of the alphabet. Before this basically sound concept could be made to work, however, the electromagnet had to be invented—that is, a device for creating a magnetic attraction by means of an electric current that could be turned on or off at will.

A Dane, Hans Oersted, was the first to discover that electricity and magnetism were related in some unknown way. (Just exactly how is not entirely understood to this day, having baffled even the brilliant Einstein.) In 1819 Oersted demonstrated that an electric current could magnetize certain materials, such as iron. Almost immediately a great Englishman, Michael Faraday, seized upon this clue and, out of it, more perhaps than any other one man, established the electronic principles upon which television rests.

In 1831 Faraday discovered induction—the strange phenomenon that an electric current in a wire can "induce" current in a nearby wire with no connection between the two. He conceived of magnetic "lines of force" radiating from the live wire in every direction. This discovery was of immense significance; it led to electric motors and generators as well as to the telegraph and all its descendants.

That same year Joseph Henry developed the first efficient

Jöns Jakob Berzelius, a 19th century Swedish chemist, discovered selenium and the photo-electric effect in 1818, which led to later advances in electronic duplication of an image.

Alessandro Volta, an Italian, invented the voltaic cell or battery in 1794 and pointed the way to control of electric currents. He is shown in a family portrait exhibiting his "pile" which was called a new "engine of research" in the development of electrical science.

Joseph Henry, an American, discovered the laws of electric induction in 1831, improved the electromagnet and made the first electric bell.

Samuel F. B. Morse invented the Morse system of telegraphy and opened the first telegraph circuit between Washington and Baltimore in 1844 with the celebrated message: "What hath God wrought?"

electromagnet, based on Faraday's principle of induction. Soon he was using it to tap out messages between two buildings at Princeton University. Thus he set the stage for Samuel F. B. Morse, who patented a long distance telegraph system in 1837 and became a hero of the American epic. An obscure art teacher at New York University, Morse perfected the hardware at the right time—when it was needed. The country was growing 3,000 miles from sea to sea, and slow communications were a serious handicap.

Morse's invention consisted of a key at the sending end, which when pressed would close an electric circuit to send an impulse along a wire. At the receiving end, an electromagnet would alternately attract or release a hinged iron bar, causing an audible click, whenever the sending key made or broke the electrical circuit. Important in the system was a simple method for translating the clicks into an alphabet, the dots and dashes of Morse code.

In England at about the same time, Sir Charles Wheatstone and William Cooke also patented a telegraph instrument. But it was Morse who had the vision and drive to sell his idea to an unbelieving, even ridiculing public. He bedeviled Congress into appropriating $30,000 to construct an experimental line of wire along the Baltimore & Ohio Railroad from Washington to Baltimore. On an historic day in May, 1844, from the U. S. Capitol, Morse clicked out the famous message, "What hath God wrought?" which was received in Baltimore.

Three days later, a dramatic coincidence banished all skepticism for good. At the Democratic National Convention in Baltimore the favored nominee for president, Martin Van Buren, was defeated by a dark horse candidate, James K. Polk. When this news was flashed to Washington over the new telegraph, cynical politicians refused to believe it. But within hours passengers arriving from Baltimore by train confirmed that Polk was indeed the candidate. The chains which for centuries had held communications to a snail's pace were broken. The incredible speed and accuracy of the telegraph were a proven fact; the days of the pony express, carrier pigeon, and semaphore were finished.

Morse's commercial success transformed the nineteenth century way of life. Telegraph lines spanned the continent, the ocean via submarine cable, finally the whole world. States and nations were drawn closer in space and time, businesses were built on the magic of the swift news flash, armies marched and countermarched in response to instantaneous orders. And now the electric sinews existed to carry any new kind of message that men might devise.

Picture transmission

Several inventors eagerly seized on the spreading network of telegraph wires to try to transmit a picture. In England, F. C. Bakewell had what he called a "copying telegraph" as early as 1847. In France, in 1862, the Italian Abbé Caselli actually sent simple drawings over a wire from Amiens to Paris. With financial backing from Napoleon III, he evolved "photo-telegrams" in the sender's own handwriting. The results were crude and unreliable, so Morse's more accurate, though painfully terse dot-and-dash telegraphy prevailed. Caselli's device was a commercial failure but it passed a milestone by making clear the nature of the problem.

If a picture is to be transmitted along a wire by a series of electrical impulses, it must first be broken up into small parts. Each impulse transmits one part. At the receiving end, the parts must be reproduced individually, then reassembled to duplicate the original picture. The process is called scanning. But how could this be done?

It adds to the romantic view of science to realize that a purely theoretical discovery of 150 years ago held the key that was to unlock the mystery. In 1818 a Swedish chemist, Baron Jöns Berzelius, isolated a new element which he called selenium (*Selene,* the moon) because it gave off a soft luminescence. Oddly, the element varied in ability to conduct electricity when exposed to various intensities of light. Berzelius thought this interesting, but went no further with his experiments. He had unknowingly discovered what we now call the "photoelectric effect."

Half a century after Berzelius, selenium found its first practical use. The Atlantic cable, laid in 1866, suffered from periodic fading of the signal. Sometimes the blackout was so complete as to render the cable useless. Grappling with the problem, a young telegrapher in Ireland named Joseph May, with no scientific background, heard about selenium from a former teacher. In 1873 he tried it in the cable circuit. Sure enough, when the selenium resister was exposed to light, the signal came in loud and clear across the ocean.

Within two years it occurred to Philip Carey, an American

In a humorous prediction for the New Year of 1879, a cartoonist for Punch, *the London weekly, combined three recent inventions of the time—the telephone, phonograph, and electric light—to get a laugh. The caption read: EDISON'S TELEPHONOSCOPE (TRANSMITS LIGHT AS WELL AS SOUND) (Every evening, before going to bed, Pater- and Mater-familias set up an electric camera-obscura over their bedroom mantel piece, and gladden their eyes with the sight of their Children at the Antipodes, and converse gaily with them through the wire.)*

Paterfamilias (in Wilton Place):
"Beatrice, come closer, I want to whisper."

Beatrice (from Ceylon): *Yes, Papa dear."*

Paterfamilias: *"Who is that charming young lady playing on Charlie's side?"*

Beatrice: *"She's just come over from England, Papa. I'll introduce you to her as soon as the game's over."*

inventor, that if the photoelectric effect could boost an electric current in proportion to a beam of light, why then in theory a picture could be transformed into various intensities of light, and the light into corresponding pulses of electricity sent along a wire. Carey designed a mosaic of selenium cells. When a picture was exposed to it, each cell would, in theory, transmit current in proportion to the darkness or lightness of the part of the picture facing it. At the receiving end, the picture could be reconstructed by causing another mosaic of selenium cells to glow in proportion to the current each cell received.

We note with some amazement that this was 1875, one year before the invention of the telephone, twenty years ahead of radio. Carey's apparatus was crude, but in 1880, Maurice Leblanc, a Frenchman interested in photography, suggested a refinement. If each part of a picture could be separately exposed in rapid succession and in proper sequence, the *illusion* of an entire picture could be

created at the receiving end. His line of thought introduced the principle of persistence of vision, upon which both the motion picture camera and the television tube depend for their effects.

In the human eye, any image received by light striking the retina persists for about one-fifteenth of a second, because of a delayed chemical reaction. Therefore, if a picture could be scanned at the rate of fifteen times (or more) per second, the eye would retain all the tiny bits and pieces long enough to assemble them into a coherent whole. The transmitted picture need not stand still. In fact, there would be no need for any "picture"—drawing or photograph—at all, because a living, moving subject could, in theory, be scanned just as well.

Television's direct ancestor

By combining these ideas, Paul Nipkow, a German engineer, designed the first true television mechanism in 1884. He used a

In 1883 cartoonists were still having fun with the "impossible" dream of transmitting distant views by some kind of electrical apparatus. These sketches imagine a young lady studying what appears to be a lesson in geometry, and (next page) a family startled to find their "camera" focused on a distant desert war — both by remote control. These may have seemed pretty far-fetched to readers, but a first direct step to television, the invention of the scanning disk, lay only one year ahead.

scanning disk with a spiral pattern of holes punched in it, which was placed before a brightly lighted picture. As the disk revolved, the first hole would cross the picture at the top. The second hole passed across the picture a little lower down, the third hole lower still, and so on. With each complete revolution of the disk, all parts of the entire picture would be briefly exposed in turn. The disk revolved fast enough to accomplish the scanning within one-fifteenth of a second, the limit of persistence of vision.

By means of lenses and mirrors the light passing through holes in the disk was guided to a selenium cell. A dark area of the picture would cause a weak current to flow from the light-sensitive cell; a bright area set up a strong current; and gray areas caused intermediate current flow. The fluctuating current was carried by a wire to a lamp, which changed in brightness according to the currents received. Now, when a second scanning disk was placed in front of the lamp, identical to the first one and revolving at the

same speed, an observer looking at the flickering lamp through the disk saw a reproduction of the original picture.

Mechanical scanning, a la Nipkow, dominated television research well into the Nineteen Twenties—for more than forty years —before it eventually proved to be a blind alley. It was difficult to synchronize the sending and receiving disks exactly, and neither the selenium cell nor the lamp were sufficiently sensitive to light changes.

Nevertheless Nipkow's invention was epochal. It proved that *a picture could be transmitted electrically* . . . way back in 1884.

Electronics

All of the nineteenth century devices described so far employed electrical circuits connected by wires. However, in 1830 Michael Faraday had demonstrated that an electric current could pass through "nothing"—actually a glass bottle from which the air had been extracted. His feat led to the deduction that electricity consisted of a stream of electrons, tiny particles that orbit the nucleus of an atom, each bearing a minute electrical charge. It was the first experimental insight into Aristotle's brilliant vision of an atomic universe.

Faraday's bottle was the great-grandfather of the vacuum tube. More sophisticated tubes followed, invented by Heinrich Geissler, a German, in 1857, and Sir William Crookes in 1878. The Crookes tube emitted rays from its cathode (negative terminal) that streamed through a vacuum to the anode (positive terminal). These "cathode rays" were in effect an electric current through empty space that could be manipulated much like current in a wire. The TV picture tube in your living room is a cathode-ray tube.

Enter Thomas Edison

In America, Thomas Alva Edison had the kind of restless mind that could not let things alone. A telegraph operator in his youth, he devised duplex, quadruple, and finally automatic telegraph systems, as well as a stock ticker. From that beginning, he branched out into a career of extraordinary fertility, producing more than 1,000 patents destined to enrich men's daily lives for centuries to come. Among these were the phonograph, the electric

Sir William Crookes, English scientist, invented the Crookes tube which demonstrated the properties of cathode rays in 1878. Today's TV picture tube utilizes this principle.

Thomas A. Edison, made a series of inventions in the 1870's and 1880's which gave birth to the phonograph, electric light, motion picture, and other marvels that were predecessors of modern television technique.

Sir Joseph J. Thomson, of England, discovered the electron and remonstrated that it was the smallest particle of the electrical structure of the atom. This was the key to twentieth century progress in communications.

light, practical methods of generating and distributing electric power, and the motion picture machine. All of these had an important, though indirect, role in the eventual creation of workable television hardware. All, as Edison well knew, were practical, money-making ideas for their own time. And yet it was one of his few "useless" inventions that proved to be crucial to the TV age.

Having lavished more than $40,000 in futile experiments before hitting upon the carbon filament electric lamp in 1879, Edison could not have been blamed for resting upon his laurels. Instead he felt the lamp could be improved and he kept trying. In one experiment he inserted a metal plate into the light bulb near the filament. When the filament grew glowing hot, a current mysteriously flowed from the plate. Edison found no practical use for this "etheric force," as he called it, but patented it anyway in 1883. Known as the "Edison effect," it was to become the basis of the modern rectifier and other radio or television tubes.

In 1885, an Englishman, Sir. J. J. Thomson, found that he could deflect a stream of cathode rays (i.e., of electrons) with a magnet. This discovery, too, like the Edison effect, lay dormant for many years. But in the twentieth century, as we shall see, it would finally provide a means for scanning a picture electronically, dispensing with Nipkow's cumbersome revolving disks.

The telephone

Another celebrated American invention of the nineteenth century, the telephone, steered the communications art in a new direction. Alexander Graham Bell, like Edison a Yankee tinkerer rather than a theoretical scientist, brought instantaneous messages directly into the home.

A handsome, intensely serious young Scot who had emigrated to Boston, Bell lectured on the articulation of speech by the deaf. He was fired with the idea that if deaf children could be made to "see" speech, they would quickly learn to talk. His researches led him to the idea of a diaphragm that would vibrate in tune with sounds reaching it. He declared, "If I can get a mechanism which will make a current of electricity vary in intensity, as the air varies in intensity when a sound is passing through it, I can telegraph any sound of speech."

One day, in 1846 in his Boston laboratory, where a pair of experimental diaphragms in different rooms were connected by a wire, Bell overturned a beaker of chemicals on his clothes. Impulsively he shouted to his assistant, "Mr. Watson! Come here, I want you!" And in the other room Watson heard Bell's voice, heard it emanating from an electronically vibrated diaphragm— the first complete sentence ever sent over a telephone wire.

Telephony created the microphone and the speaker, essential tools for sending and receiving sounds electrically whether by wire or through the air. As a thriving business, it also made possible much basic research into the sending of complex signals and reproducing them with high fidelity. Thus the modern coaxial cable, designed originally to carry hundreds of telephone conversations at once, would also become the carrier of the multiple signals required by television.

The first mass entertainment

When Edison invented that authentic miracle, the talking machine, he probably did not realize what he had started. It was one of the few truly original breakthroughs in patent history. Most inventions result from the contributions of many minds (as in the case of television), so that priority often is difficult to establish. But when Edison applied for a patent on his "speaking machine" in 1877, the U. S. Patent Office could find no prior record of anything remotely resembling it.

The phonograph made it possible to preserve sounds on a record that could be transported and replayed whenever desirable. At first Edison did not look much beyond its use as a business dictating machine. But the public insisted upon *playing* with the new toy. People were *entertained* by hearing voices and music emerging from a squawky horn in the front parlor. Suddenly, for the first time since the first minstrel twanged the first lyre, the world of entertainment came into possession of a technology that would vastly expand its audience.

What the phonograph did for sound, the motion picture did for sight. Soon after the invention of still photography in France in mid-century, attempts had been made to capture motion in the camera by shooting a series of still pictures in rapid succession. For instance, a galloping horse was photographed by half a dozen cameras set up in a line. The pictures were then mounted on a wheel and viewed in series as they whirled by. (You can still find this "Kinetoscope," usually displaying old prize fights or fan dancers, in crank-operated view boxes in a penny arcade.) Edison's contribution in 1893 was a machine for photographing a moving object in successive frames of a continuous roll of film, and then projecting the film at the same speed on a screen.

Soundless but visually entrancing, the "nickelodeon" captivated the public as nothing had since the Roman circus. It was a makeshift theater charging five cents admission to watch Edison's capering images. The center of the entertainment world began to drift from the live stage to the movie studio, from Broadway to Fort Lee, New Jersey, and thence to Hollywood, California. Audiences never larger than a few hundred or at most a few thousand for live performances grew to millions for the synthetic product. With his phonograph and his movie camera, Thomas Edison had fathered the first truly *mass* entertainment in the history of the world.

A generation fled by before the two essential elements—sound and sight—were finally joined into one medium, the talking picture, and its electronic counterpart, the television broadcast. As the nineteenth century approached its end, only one last ingredient of the TV age was still missing. This last ingredient was voice radio.

Wireless telegraphy

When telegraph poles began to march across America and the continent of Europe, it was observed that current "leaked" from the suspended wires into the air. This "leakage" mysteriously magnetized metallic objects at a considerable distance. Seeking to explain the phenomenon, James Clerk Maxwell, an English physicist, presented evidence in 1865 that the electrical impulses emitted from a live wire traveled through the air in waves similar in form and speed to light waves. Maxwell called them electromagnetic waves.

Edison, the practical man, tried to harness the waves leaking from telegraph wires. In 1885 he patented a scheme for attaching a tinfoil-covered plate (today we would call it an antenna) to a railroad locomotive. It would attract "wireless messages" from the bordering telegraph line so telegrams could be sent to people aboard a moving train. Unfortunately, the antenna attracted signals indiscriminately from all wires anywhere near the railway, creating a meaningless jumble.

This problem—how to select *one* electromagnetic wave out of the pack to carry a signal—was resolved in 1887. Heinrich Hertz, a German scientist, proved that waves could be sent out at will around an oscillating circuit. In oscillation, an electric current reverses direction at a high frequency. (For example, household alternating current in America oscillates at 60 cycles per second.) The number of cycles determines the number of waves emitted per second. They travel not in air, like sound waves, but in what Hertz called the "ether," a theoretical medium that exists even in a vacuum. A wave disseminated at a specific frequency would not mingle with waves of other frequencies.

Hertzian waves and the ether theory created great excitement in the scientific world. Sir William Crookes predicted that receiving and sending instruments would soon be devised to make possible wireless communication between remote points. He was right. He spoke in 1892. Within three years Guglielmo Marconi, a brilliant Italian youth, was ready to patent the necessary hardware.

So were born, almost simultaneously, the twentieth century, the small miracle of radio, and an age of sophisticated invention that was to lead within one generation to the larger miracle of television. Ironically, the outcome of this electrical wizardry would be to take us back to the elemental image-thinking of the earliest human beings. The medium would, indeed, prove to be the message and the massage.

Guglielmo Marconi, of Italy, sent the first wireless signals on his father's estate near Bologna in 1895, the first message between ship and shore in 1897, and the first signal across the Atlantic in 1901. Here he is pictured at his receiving station at St. John's, Newfoundland for the latter transmission.

Dr. Lee De Forest invented the audion or three-element electron tube which was later used as an oscillator to generate electromagnet (radio) waves.

2. Birth: The Twentieth Century

In New York at the witching hour of midnight, December 31, 1899, horns blew and champagne flowed in a celebration seldom matched for frantic joy. This was no ordinary New Year's Eve. Along Broadway from Union Square to 42nd Street, silk-hatted men and bejeweled women at Delmonico's, Sherry's, and Hammerstein's Paradise Roof Garden danced and drank to a new *century*. Although the merry-making was a year ahead of itself (centuries begin officially on January 1, '01), the change of number from 18— to 19— struck the spark. To Americans the twentieth century meant hope, progress, a fabulous future for a lusty nation. A famous railroad train was named after it, everything "modern" acquired the label, everything prior to 1900 became suddenly "Victorian." If you were not "twentieth century" in dress, deportment, and daring, you were old hat.

The nation was growing, thriving, feeling its oats, flexing new muscles as a world power. The Spanish-American War had planted the Stars and Stripes from Puerto Rico to Manila Bay. New President Theodore Roosevelt would make the Panama Canal an American ditch. The first automobiles were chugging about, scaring horses, and the sky would be conquered next. European immigrants were beginning to stream in by the millions, instinctively sensing a shift in the center of vitality from the Old World to the New. Americans were certain that in the twentieth century, theirs would become the greatest nation on earth.

It was a period of swift technological advances, in which the United States would soon take a commanding lead—not so much because of superior American ingenuity as of the bolder venturesomeness of American business. Others might have bright ideas, but America moved faster to put them to non-military use. At the turn of the century, that was the story of communications.

The American Marconi Company

Early in the 1890's, a teen-aged Italian of wealthy parentage, Guglielmo Marconi, had made it his life ambition to harness the newly discovered Hertzian waves as the carrier for worldwide wireless telegraphy. A scholarly youth, privately educated in Italy and England, he had both the time and the money to pursue his scientific interests. Experimenting in his father's garden, Marconi built a sending and receiving apparatus. With this equipment he succeeded in transmitting intelligible Morse code via electromagnetic waves over a short distance. Fearful that others might reach his goal before he did, young Marconi moved to England in 1896, patented his invention, and formed a company to exploit it.

Other inventors did, in fact, rush to patent offices in several countries with similar devices. But Marconi, like Samuel F. B. Morse before him, had the commercial acumen to match his scientific talent. Among his rivals was Dr. Lee De Forest, an energetic young Yale graduate who secured the approval of the United States Navy for his equipment and set up the American Wireless Telegraph Company. But Marconi's British company already had a U. S. branch, established in 1899, which sued De Forest for patent infringement and won the suit. The result was a merger in 1913 which put American Marconi Company solidly in control of radio communication. It was the predecessor of today's giant Radio Corporation of America.

The proving ground of radio was the sea—the one part of the world that could not be reached by a wire. (The submarine cable was an extension of wires from land to land.) The United States Navy, for example, was confined to signal flags, cannon shots, the heliograph (sun signals), or searchlights when ships were within visual distance; it flew homing pigeons to communicate with the shore. Accordingly, Marconi won the worldwide attention of marine interests when, in 1899, he sent a message across the English Channel. Two years later he signaled the letter "S" from Land's End, England, to St. John's, Newfoundland.

By 1903 marine wireless was in general international use. Rescues at sea dramatized its value. In 1909 Jack Binns, radio operator aboard the stricken vessel *Republic,* made world headlines by sticking to his key and summoning aid in time. The radio distress signals SOS and CQD entered our language to mean a call for help. And in 1909 it was by wireless that Robert E. Peary reported from the Arctic ice cap to an excited world, "I have found the North Pole."

While Marconi's original aim had been modeled after wire

telegraphy, i.e., transmitting a message from point to point, he actually created an entirely new type of communication: the *broadcast*. A message sent into the skies by radio traveled in all directions, to be picked up by any receiver tuned to the same wave length. The waves traveled upward as well as horizontally. At a great height they bounced off the Heaviside layer of the ionosphere and thus "around the corner" of the earth's curvature. In the development of television, this broadcast character of the signal was radio's most important contribution. It created a widely disseminated audience. Amateurs were quick to discover that with a simple, inexpensive piece of radio equipment they could enjoy the same communications art once within the capacity only of such giant organizations as Western Union and Bell Telephone. The radio "ham" of yesteryear became the TV dial twirler of today.

Words and music

Just as the dot-dash telegraph had led naturally to the voice telephone, so did "marconigrams" spark the idea of sending the human voice, musical notes, or other sounds through the ether. Reginald A. Fessenden, an American electrical enginer with Westinghouse and a professor at the University of Pittsburgh, accomplished this experimentally in 1900. He had been working on an improved detector for wireless telegraph signals. The "coherer" detector then in use was a clumsy device consisting of metal filings in a glass tube, which had to be shaken after receiving each signal in order to revive its electrical properties. (The old-time crystal detector was similar in principle, putting silica in contact with tungsten to magnify the minute electric energy of a radio wave.) Fessenden tried as a detector a miniature electric light bulb having an exceedingly fine filament. It was not commercially successful, but two things about it were significant. First, the detector was *electrical* in concept, not dependent upon imperfect natural materials such as iron filings or a silica crystal. Second, the fine filament could respond to voice undulations by delivering an undulating signal.

In England, Marconi's technical adviser, Dr. J. Ambrose Fleming, applied the 20-year-old Edison effect to the same problem. In 1904 he evolved a detector which employed the flow of electrons from filament to plate within a light bulb, as discovered by Edison, to reproduce and amplify the feeble radio currents. Fleming's was the earliest, two-element version of the vacuum tube, destined to become the heart of all radio apparatus until largely superseded in the 1960's by the transistor.

Dr. De Forest went one step further in 1906 with the "audion tube," consisting of three elements (filament, plate, and grid). The grid was a brilliant addition. Fed by a current of its own, it controlled the flow of electrons from filament to plate with great precision. Scientific historians today regard the De Forest tube as one of the key inventions of the twentieth century. It made possible the extreme magnification required for audible voice transmission by radio. In the future it would show the way toward electronic scanning of a television picture.

Television and radio

It was now 1907 and in Tsarist Russia an electrical researcher, Boris Rosing, was ready to put several pieces together. Going back more than half a century, an Englishman named Sir George Stokes had discovered the phenomenon of fluorescence. In 1852 he observed that spar (flour) a mineral used in glassmaking, would give off light when acted upon by radiant energy. In 1897 Karl Braun, a German, added a fluorescent inner surface to a Crookes (cathode-ray) tube. Sure enough, it glowed when struck by the rays. Rosing, familiar with the frustrating attempts of Carey, Nipkow, and others to scan a picture for transmission, seized upon the Braun tube as a possible answer. He set up, in principle at least, what was probably the first complete system for electronic television via wireless. Had he lived in some country other than Russia, already in a state of political and economic decay rumbling with revolution, Rosing might well have brought his experiments to practical fruition.

Instead, other scientists working in the same field, on the same problem, at the same time, picked up the baton. This would be the situation in the early 1920's. While a young man from Idaho, Philo Farnsworth, was developing a television system which centered in a camera called the "image dissector," another young man newly arrived from Russia, Vladimir Zworykin (who would become an American citizen), was perfecting his own television camera which he called the "iconoscope." The interesting thing is that both men were influenced by Boris Rosing. Farmsworth read an account of the Russian's experiments in an American popular scientific magazine,

Vladimir K. Zworykin, a Russian-born American citizen, invented the iconoscope in 1923 and developed the kinescope later as the essential ingredients of an all-electronic television system. In this picture he is holding the iconoscope or "eye" of early TV cameras.

while Zworkykin as a graduate student in Russia had actually worked as Rosing's assistant.

It was World War I and revolutionary upheaval that led Zworykin to emigrate to the United States, but in all other respects the war stopped television in its tracks. It did just the opposite for radio. Hundreds of radio hams were active in the United States, while the armies of the belligerents were rapidly developing the new medium for transmitting intelligence. A great postwar future was predicted for radio (or wireless) but primarily as a means of communicating with ships and airplanes, sending press dispatches (the New York *Times* received the first transatlantic one in 1907), and exchanging messages over very long distances. Few foresaw the broadcasting of entertainment. One outstanding exception was David Sarnoff.

In 1912, as a young wireless operator, Sarnoff made a name for himself when he received the first news of the *Titanic's* catastrophic collision with an iceberg. For 72 hours Sarnoff stayed at his set, relaying the names of survivors from the rescue ship *Carpathia* as it approached New York. Sarnoff moved upward in the American Marconi Company organization. Four years later, in 1916, he was writing this memorandum to his superiors:

> I have in mind a plan of development which would make radio a household utility. The idea is to bring music into the home by wireless. The receiver can be designed in the form of a simple "radio music box" and arranged for several different wave lengths which should be changeable with the throwing of a single switch or the pressing of a single button. The same principle can be extended to numerous other fields, as for example, receiving lectures at home which would be perfectly audible. Also, events of national importance can be simultaneously announced and received. Baseball scores can be transmitted in the air. This proposition would be especially interesting to farmers and others living in outlying districts.

Perhaps young Sarnoff had been reading *Looking Backward,* the famous novel of the Eighties in which Edward Bellamy predicted music and lectures in every home, but by wire, not wireless, and not until A.D. 2000! Sarnoff's employers must have found his ideas equally visionary. In 1919 when the Radio Corporation of America was founded to acquire the assets of American Marconi, and Sarnoff remained with the new company as a junior executive,

David Sarnoff (left), started out in life as a wireless operator working with the Marconi system of radio and rose to become chairman of the board of RCA. He is pictured here with Guglielmo Marconi.

John L. Baird, English electrical engineer, demonstrated a mechanical system of television in 1925, and made the first daily transmissions over B.B.C., London beginning in 1929.

RCA stated its purpose as achieving U. S. preeminence in worldwide communications. That is, in messages, not in entertainment, lectures, or airborne journalism. But Sarnoff would not go without honor in his own company. In 1926 as vice-president of RCA, he established the National Broadcasting Company. Every single word of his prophecy had come true.

The Twenties

World War I did not, as we now know to our sorrow, make the world safe for democracy, but it did establish the United States at the top of what was left. The most advanced nations of Europe lay in ruins, if not physically then financially. They were politically and socially unstable. In the United States the energetic and ambitious individual could still see a rewarding future. The brains of the world now joined the tide of transatlantic emigration, and America was the beneficiary. In the field of electronic communication, it would be impossible to measure the contributions of immigrant scientists to the scores of "minor" inventions that comprise modern engineering advances. This much is certain; technological progress in television became concentrated in two countries, the U.S.A. and England.

In the latter country, John Logie Baird made the first public demonstration of wireless television early in the decade, forming the first company exclusively devoted to the new art. In the United States, mineral and chemical substances were discovered which proved to be more sensitive to light than selenium and more fluorescent than fluor. In combination with a Swedish invention of 1910, A. Elkstrom's "flying spot" (a strong light beam for scanning an object before the camera), these elements promised to supplant the inadequacy of television scanning with quicker and clearer sight. Meanwhile the basic TV receiver, now being called a "kinescope," was evolving out of the Braun tube. Technically described as a cathode-ray oscillograph, it caused a stream of electrons, controlled by the incoming signals, to sweep over a fluorescent screen (i.e., scan it) in response to a varying magnetic field.

Radio now was proliferating like a colony of jack rabbits. The scary but short postwar depression of 1920–1921 scarcely dented the boom. Good times came back with a rush. There was work for everyone who wanted work, and the stock market headed for outer space. In 1920 and 1921, pioneer radio stations began broadcasting phonograph records and news. Among these were KDKA, the Westinghouse station in Pittsburgh, which received the first commercial license from the Department of Commerce; WWJ, operated by the Detroit *News;* and WJZ (now WABC), in Newark, New Jersey.

KDKA held its grand opening on election night, November 2, 1920, to broadcast returns of the Harding-Cox presidential race. People lacking their own radio sets gathered in the halls and movie theatres throughout the area to hear. This program is generally considered the historic beginning of commercial, or at least, non-experimental broadcasting. Others like it, such as President Harding's inauguration and the Dempsey-Carpentier heavyweight championship fight, set off a rush to stores to buy radio sets. Sales grew so fast that the manufacturers could not meet the demand.

The insatiable market also stimulated technology. Major Edwin Armstrong, inventor of the regenerative (signal-magnifying) radio circuit in 1913, followed it up in 1920 with the basic superheterodyne. This quickly put the crystal set completely out of style, and substituted a loud speaker for the earlier earphones. David Sarnoff's "radio music box" became a reality for family listening. Phonographs and records came close to expiring as a business because of radio competition for listeners' attention.

The broadcasting boom

The business structure of mass communications began to take shape. As set ownership grew into the millions, advertisers ready with products to sell took a hard look at the new marketplace. Radio stations expanded into networks, and the networks into news-gathering agencies rivaling the newspaper wire services. Actors, comedians, theatrical producers, directors, writers, musicians swarmed into the new field to create and provide entertainment. Audiences swelled to the tens of millions. Some radio shows attained such popularity that, each weekday night, listening to *Amos 'n' Andy* almost brought all other everyday activity to a halt throughout America between 7:00 and 7:15 P.M., Eastern Standard Time.

Since television by this time had been pretty well worked out in principle, we may wonder at its neglect during the period of radio's spectacular growth. There were two reasons. Radio broadcast-

THE RADIO KINEMA

by F. H. ROBINSON

Not so very long ago I visited one John Logie Baird at his laboratory at Hastings, and saw a demonstration which proved that he has proceeded so far along the road to radio vision as to make it almost a commercial proposition, for the whole of the apparatus used in the experiment about to be described could have been purchased for £40.

The apparatus used can be applied to wire or wireless transmitters with ease and without the alteration of anything further than the microphone, in which circuit the "Radio Vision" machine is connected.

The Test.

I myself saw a cross, the letter "H," and the fingers of my own hand reproduced by this apparatus across the width of the laboratory. The images were quite sharp and clear, although perhaps a little unsteady. This, however, was mostly due to mechanical defects in the apparatus and not to any fault of the system.

Moving images may be transmitted by this means, and distance is no object, merely depending on the power of the wireless transmitter and the sensitivity of the receiver employed.

It is possible that machine-made apparatus on the lines indicated above could be made for some £50, which would be capable of transmitting letters and words clearly many miles through the ether, and all that appears to be necessary in order to reproduce and transmit moving pictures is more expensive and elaborate apparatus.

The inventor is confident that no technical difficulties stand in the way of the transmission of moving images by wireless.

Undoubtedly wonderful possibilities are opened up by this invention, its very simplicity and reliability placing it well to the front of many of the various complicated methods which have been evolved to do the same work.

One of the earliest press reports of television was this account of "one John Logie Baird at his laboratory at Hastings," which appeared in the Kinematograph Weekly of London in April, 1924. The writer marveled that he saw the fingers of his own hand "reproduced by this apparatus across the width of the laboratory." The publicity led to financial backing for Baird, a shy Scotsman in poor health, from Will Day, a pioneer promoter of the British film industry.

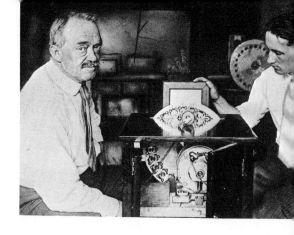

ing was relatively simple and inexpensive, both for transmitter and receiver. Facilities for television would be complex and costly. In the electronic systems developed by Zworykin, Farnsworth, Baird, *et al.,* each function such as scanning, synchronization, or sound required its own carrier impulse. Carried by wire, a TV program would need cables equivalent to telephone wiring for fifteen simultaneous conversations. Carried by wireless, it needed a cluster of wavelengths, not just one.

Secondly, voice radio was spectacularly successful with a public still innocent of television. It was creating overnight fortunes for set manufacturers, broadcasters, advertising agencies. In show business it would make multi-millionaires of popular performers like Rudy Vallee, Bing Crosby, Bob Hope, and Jack Benny. No one was in any hurry to rock the boat. In other words, the problem was one of money investment and of disentangling the crowded air waves by government regulation, rather than one of science. Pending its solution, TV engineers temporarily turned the clock back to mechanical scanning.

Early television experimenters in 1925, using a mechanical scanning disk. The engineer holds in his right hand the picture to be tele-vised, while his left hand operates a control button. The image was picked up through the rotating disk by a light-sensitive cell on the top of the cabinet.

Some television pioneers

In 1923, the same year that Zworykin, now of Wilkinsburg, Pennsylvania, applied for a patent on his iconoscope TV camera, C. Francis Jenkins transmitted a mechanically-scanned still photo of President Harding from his Washington, D.C., laboratory to Philadelphia—about 130 air miles. Two years later Jenkins made the first telecast of a moving object, from a radio station on the Washington outskirts to his laboratory receiver. Also in 1925, Dr. Herbert E. Ives of Bell Telephone Laboratories outlined a television research program for the telephone industry. Within a year his group was transmitting motion picture films over a miniature television hookup.

In 1927 Ives made a public demonstration that struck observers as miraculous. A tap dancer strutting her stuff on the roof of Bell's New York skyscraper (that is, in bright sunshine) could be clearly observed on a tiny screen in Ives's office on a floor below. The image, carried by telephone wires, was seen through a Nipkow-like scanning disk. Its light source was a gas-filled neon lamp, then only recently invented, which unlike filament lamps had the property of instantly changing in brightness according to variations in current

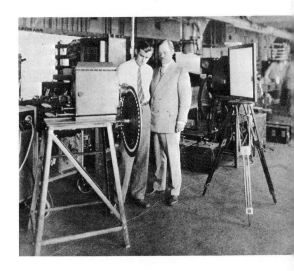

Dr. E. F. W. Alexanderson of General Electric was one of the leading pioneers in the early days of television. He appears here (right) with an associate, Ray D. Kell, inspecting the mechanical scanning disk during experiments in Schenectady, N. Y. in 1927.

Major Edward H. Armstrong developed the regenerative and super-heterodyne circuits that made radio broadcasting practical and demonstrated the first frequency modulation system in 1935 with transmissions from Alpine, New Jersey, to New York. He is thus known as the father of FM and of TV sound.

29

Dr. E. F. Alexanderson of General Electric Company demonstrating the first home television receiver on January 23, 1928. He holds a control button to regulate the scanning disk inside the receiver, and to synchronize its speed with that of the transmitting disk and the sound. It produced a 3-inch image.

received. (It was this demonstration that inspired the Sunday feature article mentioned in our Introduction.)

Meanwhile, at the General Electric Company in Schenectady, New York, Dr., E. F. W. Alexanderson was trying to do the same thing by wireless. On December 16, 1926, the nation's press devoted much space to a report from St. Louis where, at a meeting of the American Institute of Electrical Engineers, Dr. Alexanderson described his system. It used revolving mirrors to project a television image of motion pictures on a screen. The scientist was quoted as saying that the world might one day "view the Rajah of India on parade, a future world championship boxing match, or heads of nations may hold a conference by television."

An improved scanning disc soon proved superior to revolving mirrors, although the question of wire versus wireless transmission remained unresolved. The 48 holes in the disc were enlarged and each fitted with a glass magnifying lens. The object being televised, brilliantly lighted, was placed in front of the disc, which revolved twenty times each second. The reflected light passing through the disc activated a number of photoelectric cells, or "electric eyes," that had potassium coatings much more sensitive than Nipkow's primitive selenium cells. The potassium emitted electrons in fairly precise proportion to the varying light passing through each hole, thus converting it into a series of small electric impulses ready for broadcasting.

Dr. Alexanderson's prototype home television receiver—America's first—was about the size of the old style console phonograph. It contained a disc similar to the one used in the transmitter. As the radio impulses were received, they were changed back into varying intensities of light by a specially built high-frequency neon lamp. As the neon light was viewed through the holes in the revolving disc, a picture about three inches square appeared to the eye. Alexanderson had to keep manipulating a special control knob so as to hold the disc's speed in synchronization with the transmitter. In 1928, using the improved disc and an enlarging mirror for viewing, Alexanderson was able to bring the picture up to fourteen inches square. This proved an outstanding attraction at the New York Radio Show in September.

The Ives telephone group scored on April 7, 1927, with the first transmission of sound and scene over a considerable distance. Flickering to life on a screen in the New York laboratory was a talking image of Herbert Clark Hoover, then Secretary of Commerce, flashed over a pair of telephone wires from Washington. The President-to-be thus played a starring role in the first intercity live television "show" in history. Later in the year the first television variety show was transmitted a distance of approximately 200 miles. People in the know were now convinced that television had a future. On May 10, 1928, the first regular programs were telecast from the General Electric station, WGY Schenectady, and continued three times a week. This was done mostly for the benefit of a few engineers and enthusiasts who owned Alexanderson receivers, and to help promote the medium.

Short wave radio was used in 1928 for the first television transoceanic broadcast. A picture of a Mrs. Mia Howe was sent into the ether by the Baird Television Development Company from station 2KZ, Purley, England, and received at Hartsdale, New York, by amateur station W2CVJ. The feat was significant in showing that short (high frequency) waves could be the answer to TV's need for a multi-frequency "channel." Eventually the U. S. Government was to assign very high frequency (VHF) and later ultrahigh frequency (UHF) waves to television development, leaving radio undisturbed in the "long" and ordinary "short" wave bands.

WGY experimentally broadcast the first television drama on September 11, 1928, entitled *The Queen's Messenger*. Two TV cameras were used, one to pick up the face of the person speaking and the other the props of the play. The same station also accomplished the first remote pickup of news by television from the steps of the State Capitol in Albany, New York. It aired both the image and the voice of Governor Alfred E. Smith as he delivered his speech of acceptance of the Democratic nomination for president in August .

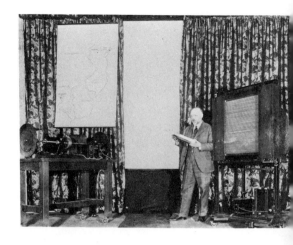

This apparatus was used for the first public demonstration of intercity television on April 7, 1927. Herbert Hoover, Secretary of Commerce in Washington, spoke with and saw Walter S. Gifford, president of A.T.&T., over telephone wires in New York. In the photo Dr. Herbert E. Ives of Bell Telephone Laboratories is holding a photoelectric cell from the transmitter, shown at left. The receiving screen at right consisted of 50 neon-filled tubes divided into small segments. Electric impulses from the transmitter, controlled by a scanning disk, energized the segments to create a pattern of light and dark areas which composed the picture.

The birth of CBS

On September 18, 1927, the Columbia Phonograph Broadcasting System broadcast *The King's Henchmen* by radio from the Metropolitan Opera House with Deems Taylor, the composer, as commentator. This prestigious introduction of a new network was the result of a competitive situation faced by the makers of Columbia phonographs and records. In 1926 RCA had formed the National Broadcasting Company with two networks, the Red and

The back of the Bell Telephone TV receiver of 1927 consisted of hundreds of wires, each connected to a different segment of the pattern of neon tubes on the face of the receiver. A motor-driven commutator, synchronized with the scanning disk, sent current through each wire in turn. Electronic scanning and picture tubes eliminated this clumsy apparatus.

the Blue, and was about to merge with the Victor Talking Machine Company, Columbia's major competitor. Columbia countered by entering radio. It acquired United Independent Broadcasters, a rather shaky enterprise formed earlier in the year by, among others, Arthur Judson, the concert manager, and Major J. Andrew White, a radio pioneer.

The phonograph company soon bowed out of the network venture, though its name remained. One achievement was a radio show called the *La Palina Smoker* for the Congress Cigar Company of Philadelphia, headed by Samuel Paley. His son and advertising manager, William S. Paley, impressed by the boost in cigar sales, became convinced that radio had a great future. Young Paley persuaded his family to buy into the new company for $450,000. With-

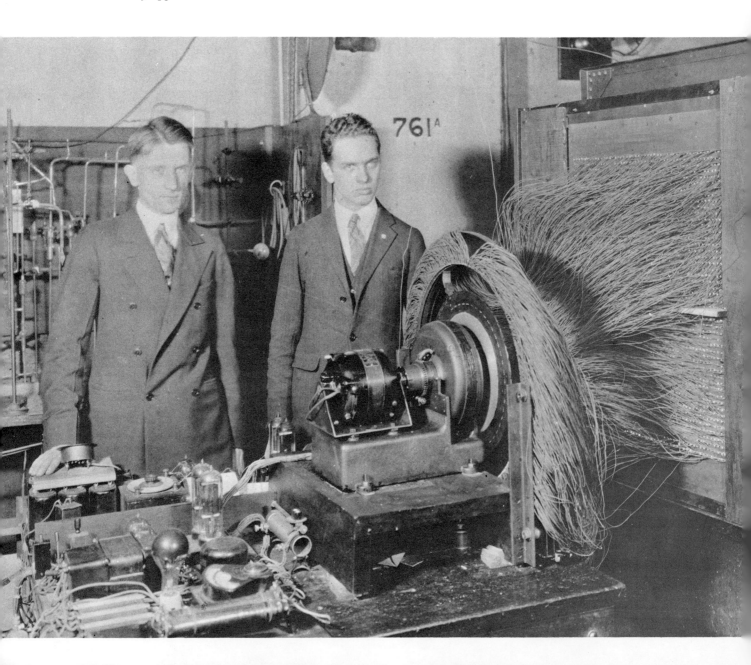

in a few months he had merged the various interests and on January 3, 1929, at the age of 27, became president of the renamed Columbia Broadcasting System.

In his first year, Paley negotiated a deal with Adolph Zukor of Paramount Publix Corporation which gave CBS access to Hollywood talent and improved the drawing power of its programs. That early alliance between radio broadcasting and film production was to become an important force in the future direction of television. The success of CBS also gave NBC a forceful rival. So began the fierce competitiveness that characterizes American broadcasting, in contrast to the government ownership or near-monopoly of the air-waves prevalent in most other countries.

That same year, 1929, the Bell Telephone Laboratories held the first demonstration of television in color. Some of the pictures shown were an American flag, a watermelon, and a bunch of roses. The system had three separate sets of photo-electric cells, amplifiers, and glow tubes, each filtering out one color—red, blue, or green. At the receiving end, mirrors superimposed the three monochromatic images to make one picture in color. But it utilized mechanical scanning and was of low definition.

Probably the most important event for television that year was Vladimir Zworykin's appearance before a meeting of the Institute of Radio Engineers in Rochester, New York. There he demonstrated a kinescope or cathode-ray television receiver—the mate to his iconoscope TV camera for transmitting images. Clearly it meant that RCA, for whom Zworykin now worked, had access to a complete, workable television system along with the financial resources to exploit it.

But the decade ended in financial disaster—the great Wall Street crash and panic of October 1929. Even then few realized the depth of the depression that would follow. If all that television needed now was money and business enterprise, it would have a long wait. The technology was virtually complete, but the economic omens were poor and would get worse.

The Thirties

Reflecting the gloom of the depression years, the *Encyclopedia Britannica* article on television written in 1931 by Dr. Herbert E. Ives took a cautious tone. Summing up the state of the art, Ives

mentioned such exciting prospects as "displaying speakers or athletic events to audiences at a distant point," and then added:

> At the present time, while all of these possibilities as well as some special developments, such as television in color, have been experimentally demonstrated, the practical and economic barriers to transmitting really satisfactory images are so great as to oppose very serious obstacles to the general use of television . . . There is no clear answer as yet whether television may ultimately be expected to compare in value with sound broadcasting . . . Whether a working compromise will be attained in which *the value of the simultaneity of the event and viewing, which is the essence of television,* will be great enough to offset the crudity of a commercially possible picture, is for the future to disclose. (Italics ours.)

The experimentation continued and gathered momentum, but the first big breakthrough would not come until 1936, and in Dr. Ives's own field, telephone communication. A coaxial cable was laid between New York and Philadelphia as a joint experiment of the American Telephone and Telegraph Company with the Philadelphia Electric Storage Battery Company ("Philco"), a leading manufacturer of radio sets. This cable, consisting of wires suspended at the center of a hollow tube, carried simultaneous electrical impulses of different frequencies without jumbling them. A. T. & T. was interested in the possibility of carrying up to 600

This was the CBS television studio of 1930, using the "flying spot" type of camera pickup. The strong lights made the small room insufferably hot.

In 1928 General Electric station WYG, Schenectady, N.Y., televised Governor Alfred E. Smith as he delivered his speech of acceptance for the Democratic presidential nomination. This was the beginning of TV convention reporting. Not until 1932, when F. D. Roosevelt broke precedent, did the nominee address a convention in person, and the first TV camera did not penetrate a convention floor until 1940.

separate telegraph messages at once. Philco was interested in better transmission of radio and eventually TV network programs.

Not many listeners are aware that radio broadcasts seldom travel through the air exclusively. Most of them are sent part way over telephone wires connecting the studio or point of origin with the transmitting station. Until the development of microwave relays, many years later, transcontinental radio-TV depended entirely upon telephone connections.

The second big breakthrough for television would come near the end of this troubled decade. In the American system, the people "own" the air-waves, and the Government distributes licenses to private enterprise to use them. The need for regulation had become evident in radio's early days, in order to allocate wavelengths and prevent broadcasting stations from interfering with one another's signals. Television raised new technical problems which placed the Government in a delicate quandary. The *kind* of equipment employed would determine *how* TV would be sent and received, but there were several rival systems. Vladimir Zworykin's patents were

The iconoscope of 1923, invented by Vladimir Zworykin, provided the first means of scanning a scene electronically, basic principle of the modern television camera.

in litigation for years; it was not at all clear whether his iconoscope camera or Philo Farnsworth's image dissector, introduced in 1928, would (or should) prevail. Behind the scenes, powerful companies fought for the incalculable future prize.

On the first day of 1939, the issue would be settled by granting Zworykin, of RCA, a patent for his iconoscope (sending) and kinescope (receiving) tubes, the basis for modern, fully electronic TV. Only then would mechanical scanning finally go into the ashcan; the picture "crudity" of which Dr. Ives complained would become past history. The legal decision would also lead to mergers and cross-licensing agreements which combined many competing technological improvements into a standard type of sending and receiving equipment available to all.

Experimental TV

In July 1930, NBC opened experimental television station W2XBS in New York, followed by W2XAB, a CBS station, in 1931. The inaugural broadcasts were each prophetic of things to come. NBC demonstrated a new type of receiver that projected a picture 6 x 8 feet on the screen at RKO Proctor's 58th Street Theater in New York. It failed to arouse much enthusiasm; the picture was blurred, to the annoyance of the audience. But note the combination of show-business traditions: NBC (radio), RKO (movies), and Proctor's (vaudeville). The CBS kick-off was a gala occasion, the earliest hint of a TV "spectacular." Mayor James J. Walker officially opened the station. Kate Smith sang her famous radio theme song, "When the Moon Comes Over the Mountain." George Gershwin played "Lisa" on the piano. Other radio favorites were at last seen as well as heard.

Allen B. DuMont promoted the idea of home (rather than

In 1930 Felix the Cat whirled for hours on a phonograph turntable in front of television scanners, while RCA engineers in their homes made reception tests. The rig to the left of the scanning camera was the complete transmitter of experimental station W2XBS, the predecessor of WNBT and WNBC–TV.

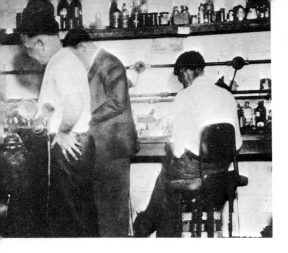

One of the first commercially practical cathode ray television tubes was developed by Dr. Allen B. DuMont in the basement laboratory of his home in New Jersey. This is an actual picture of the work in progress in 1931.

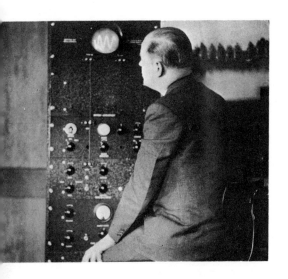

Wave forms are observed by Dr. Allen B. DuMont on his first television transmitter in the early Thirties. At that time only a few thousand receivers existed throughout the New York metropolitan area.

theatre) TV reception with a half-hour program on August 20, 1930, broadcast from W2XCR, Jersey City, and W2XCD, Passaic, New Jersey. Performers Harry Hershfield, George Jessel, Arthur (Bugs) Baer, Benny Rubin, and Diana Seaby appeared on screens placed in a hotel room, an office, and an apartment in New York City. In April of the same year, A. T. & T. demonstrated two-way television. Persons in two of the company's New York buildings, separated by a considerable distance, were able to talk to and see each other as if at opposite sides of a table.

During this period, transmitted signals were sadly lacking in sharpness. The flickering, fuzzy pictures could excite only an enthusiast, just as feeble sounds in the earphone had excited crystal-set radio amateurs a decade earlier. A picture was made up of roughly 60 lines as compared to 525 lines today. In 1931 RCA boosted the definition to 125 lines, and built a TV antenna atop the Empire State Building, the world's tallest skyscraper (where it still is).

By 1935 higher quality pictures of 245 lines were being transmitted by General Electric. But mechanical scanning had limitations that no amount of precision could quite overcome. Electronic scanning waited in the wings, and so did the TV audience. A remarkably lucid summary of where television stood in public estimation appeared in 1936 in a book, *The Next Hundred Years,* by J. C. Furnas. He wrote:

Television, when and if, depends at both ends on the photocell. The talk of television among the experts is, on the whole, pessimistic. "It will be a long time" is the gist of the statements. There are always a few optimists who say, "Next year. Television in every third home. Satisfactory." Still the years roll on. Each one brings something new, but no one has yet solved all the difficulties. The movie people struggled for 30 years to get a little sound in their performances and the sound people (radio) have been working just as hard and almost as long to get a little vision in their act.

The trouble lies in the way our senses respond. We hear only one thing at a time. A conglomerate of noises when all put together give one sound wave which can be caught as a single wriggly line on a wax record which can then give almost perfect reproduction. Sound is one thing after another but it is only one impression at a time.

Sight is a composite of a multitude of impressions at one time. The eye does not scan one infinitesimal part of a picture for an instant and then go on to the next segment. That is what happens with the ear but not with the eye. The eye takes it all in at once, thousands of minute impressions on thousands of minute sensitive screens at the back of the retina. If you are to have television you must transmit thousands of separate impressions at one time—or almost at one time—while one impulse at a time is all that sound requires. It is easy to see why the experts are pessimistic.

The principle of the clumsy mechanical scanning disk, first used for television, dates back to 1884. The idea lay fallow for 40 years and then came to light in a partnership with modern photo-electric cells to produce a minute and jumpy laboratory image, literally a peek at a time, but the peeks were so rapid that to the eye they were almost a continuous picture. The scanning disk was quicker than the eye. However, the transmitted images have never been really clear or sharp.

Something distinctly new has come along in the development of a device burdened with the name iconoscope . . . the photo-cell counterpart of the human eye. It includes a sensitive screen which in effect contains millions of tiny photo-cells. That is really what the human eye is except that the eye-cells are tied to nerves instead of electric wires. When this iconoscope televises, it scans the whole image with a roving beam of electrons and at the receiving end the 'scope translates impulses into lights and shadows, giving the whole picture practically instantaneously. The number of wire or radio circuits required depends upon the desired sharpness of the image. There are no particular limitations to image size. Another important contribution is the improved system of multiple simultaneous messages on one wire. This greatly reduces the complexity of transmission systems required for television.

These devices make satisfactory television seem closer. The date of its reality probably depends on the buying public and engineering ingenuity. We have quite a bit of both. It is my hope, and I see no reason why it should not be realized, to be able to go to an ordinary movie theatre when some great national event is taking place across the country and see on the screen the sharp image of the action reproduced—at the same instant it occurs. This waiting for the newsreels to come out is a bit tiresome for the twentieth century. Some time later I hope to be able to take my inaugurals, prize fights, and football games at home. I expect

Dr. DuMont, the television pioneer, holding a 14-inch television picture tube which his company made in 1938, for use in the first electronic receiver marketed in the United States.

This 1938 DuMont receiver was the first all-electronic television set on the market in the United States. Called the "Clifton," after the location of the manufacturer in Clifton, New Jersey, it had a 14-inch tube, huge for its day.

to do it satisfactorily and cheaply. Only under those conditions can a television get into my house. I do not know how soon it will be but it is the most important item of unfinished business.

I am waiting for my television but I cannot live forever. When I think that the first radio impulse transmission was accomplished by Joseph Henry in 1840 and the first radio broadcast was not until 1920, I feel a little discouraged about the arrival of this television business while my eyes still function. No one has dared even to think of television in natural colors as yet.

Possibly in anticipation of the Zworykin patent decision, experimental TV now went into high gear. Programs began to flow from New York over the coaxial cable to Philadelphia; and on June 29, 1936, a high definition telecast—343 lines, 30 pictures per second—emanated from the Empire State antenna.

In 1931, NBC began transmitting from on top of the Empire State Building with new 120–line television. The pictures compare the definition of the earlier 60–line screen, at left, with the 120–line screen.

One of the first RCA home television receivers was this 1937 model with a mirror on the cover, which reflected the image from a flat screen so it could be seen from all points in a room.

The first remote unit began roaming the streets of New York for NBC in 1937. A microwave transmitter inside the bus relayed picture signals to the Empire State Building for rebroadcast.

In 1937 an electronic projection "gun" made possible images of movie-screen size, and at Christmas NBC put the first mobile TV unit out on the streets of New York. It used a microwave transmitter in a truck to relay electronic images to the Empire State Building for rebroadcast. This unit, a year later, happened to be taking pictures at a swimming pool on an island in the East River. Suddenly a fire broke out in an abandoned barracks. The mobile unit turned its cameras on the first unscheduled news event ever televised.

A big event in 1938 was the telecast over W2XBS of Rachel Crothers' comedy, *Susan and God,* with the original Broadway cast. Exact replicas of the stage settings were constructed in the NBC radio studio, where Gertrude Lawrence, Paul McGrath, and Nancy Coleman repeated their lines without a hitch. That same year Du Mont began manufacturing TV receivers on an assembly line. An audience was beginning to take shape, at first only the "in" crowd who, like first-nighters on Broadway, always want to be first with something new. To enlarge them to a mass audience, the industry set its sights on the New York World's Fair.

The first big success

The Fair opened on Flushing Meadow on April 30, 1939, around a Trylon and a Perisphere symbolizing "The World of Tomorrow." The theme was amply fulfilled. Few who saw it will

forget General Motors' exhibit of "futuristic" roads, thrilling then but commonplace today in America's network of expressways. The same bug-eyed crowds ooh-ed and ah-ed over futuristic television. The formal opening of the Fair was telecast by NBC, including an address by President Franklin D. Roosevelt—the first head of state ever to be seen by a television audience. Six weeks later, the King and Queen of England were likewise telecast, on their visit to the Fair for "British Week."

Within a few months Hitler's panzers and stukas would be thundering into Poland and the world would be at war.

Many of the foreign exhibits at the Fair would sadly close their doors and pack up for home. This war would again stop television in its tracks, as another war had done a generation earlier. But no one knew that yet, and the broadcasters intensified their efforts to create crowd-pleasing program material.

One item was the first studio variety show, telecast by NBC from Radio City. The entertainment included Fred Waring and his Pennsylvanians, Macy Westcott and Richard Rodgers, Marjorie Clarke, Earl Larimore, and David More, some interviews from the World's Fair, and a "Donald Duck" cartoon. Other "firsts" followed in swift succession; the first televised baseball game, between Columbia and Princeton at Baker Field, New York, announced by Bill Stern; a professional game between Brooklyn and Cincinnati at Ebbets Field; a fashion show; part of the six-day bicycle race at Madison Square Garden; a professional boxing match between Lou Nova and Max Baer at Yankee Stadium. Football came in with a game between Fordham and Waynesburg College; also tennis; musical comedy; Gilbert and Sullivan; and the first full-length feature film on the air, *The Heart of New York*.

TV entertainment was building up to a cornucopia of goodies as the decade came to a close. There was even something for the kiddies, Macy's annual Thanksgiving Day parade. For industry there was the first closed-circuit telecast, December 8, 1939, of assembled leaders of the International Rotary at the studio of W2XB, Schenectady, to be seen and heard simultaneously by Rotarians at dinners in Schenectady, Albany, and Troy.

Also prophetic of things to come was the emergence of TV's first enduring "personality." He was Dennis James, who began in 1938 as the master of ceremonies for DuMont's experimental programs. The studio was a small room on Madison Avenue where

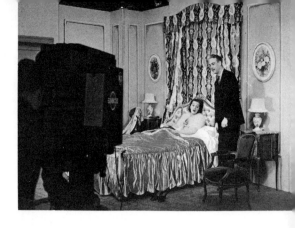

A big event for television in 1938 was a telecast of scenes from Rachel Crothers' "Susan and God" with the original Broadway cast and exact replicas of the stage sets. Starred in the hit play were Gertrude Lawrence and Paul McGrath.

The first unscheduled news event on television was a fire on Ward's Island, New York City, in November 1938. An NBC mobile unit happened to be working at a swimming pool just across the river, and turned its camera on the flames. Newspapers throughout the country picked up this picture directly from the TV screen.

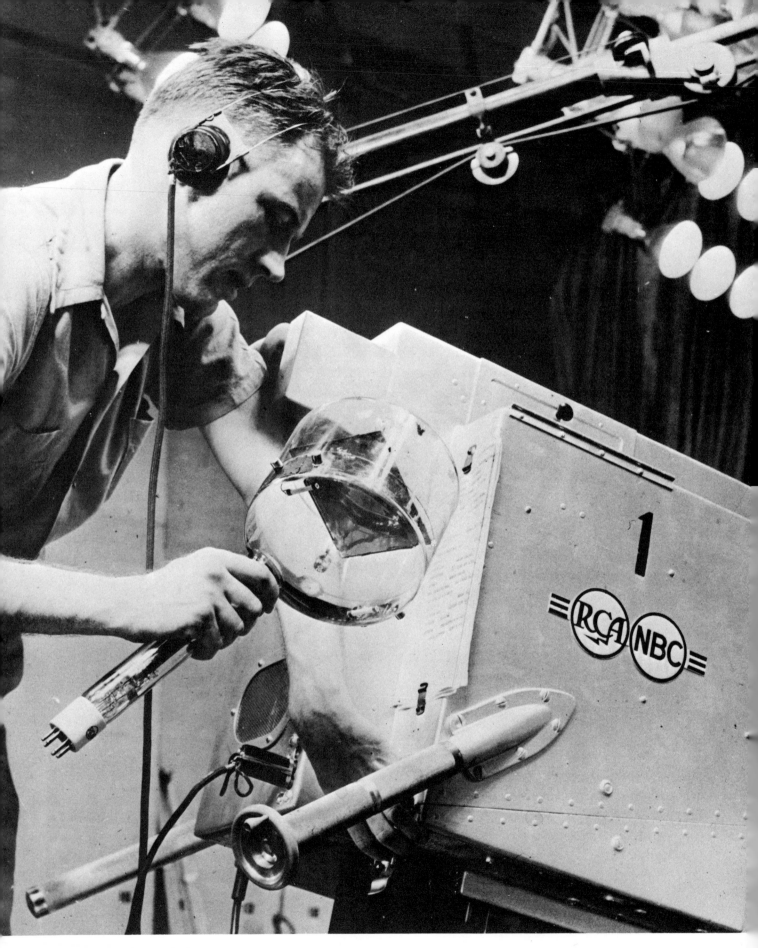

The iconoscope, when put into the camera, gave television its electronic eye. The granting of this RCA patent early in 1939, after 15 years of litigation, came just in time for public promotion of home TV at the New York World's Fair.

the Klieg lights raised a murderous temperature of 140 degrees, while the audience consisted of a couple of hundred set owners in the New York area. James was the announcer who, ten years later, would make wrestling fans of middle-aged women and who became the darling of daytime quiz and game shows. He continued entertaining the ladies via TV well into the Sixties.

On the eve of the Forties the United States had exactly two years to go before this nation, too, would be forced to concentrate on guns instead of butter. Television made the most of its brief opportunity. When the lights went out at Pearl Harbor December 7, 1941, the new medium was technically and economically ready for a great leap forward. But it would remain poised in that position, a runner awaiting the starter's gun, for five long years.

In April 1939 David Sarnoff, then president of RCA, dedicated the RCA Building at the New York World's Fair in front of NBC's television camera. The Fair drew mass attention to the new art, but progress was cut short by the advent of World War II.

Franklin D. Roosevelt was the first President to be televised, in ceremonies opening the New York World's Fair in April, 1939. The picture was fuzzy but recognizable.

45

3. Infant Prodigy: The Forties

In the year 1940, the United States alternately recoiled from an Old World seemingly intent on blowing itself off the face of the map, and warily drew closer as its own interests became inevitably embroiled. The nation split down the middle in a propaganda war between the America First Committee, isolationist, and the Committee to Defend America by Aiding the Allies. In May France fell before Hitler's hordes, the British Army fled from Dunkirk, and only the heroism of the RAF in the Battle of Britain saved democracy's last bastion from invasion. What brought the World War home to America was radio, now at the very pinnacle of its power.

Broadcasting for the first time as Prime Minister, Winston Churchill promised to fight, "on the beaches, in the fields . . . we shall never surrender," until the New World would see fit to come to the rescue. "This . . . is . . . London," intoned the memorable voice of Edward R. Murrow as the Luftwaffe rained fire bombs on the helpless population. America listened to radio as never before, horrified, fascinated, deeply disturbed. Short-wave sets for trans-oceanic listening were in heavy demand. It was, to paraphrase Churchill, radio's finest hour. Television, that newfangled toy, was all but forgotten.

President Roosevelt announced his intention to run for a precedent-shattering third term. The Depression was over, its back broken by new jobs in war industry. People rushed to buy automobiles and other consumer goods as if there would be no tomorrow. Selective Service, the first peacetime draft, inspired Danny Kaye to sing *Melody in 4-F*. At the Republican National Convention in Philadelphia, gallery crowds overwhelmed the professional politicians with chants of "We want Willkie!" until, unbelievably, their hero was nominated. A businessman who had built his following on opposition to the domestic policies of the New Deal, Wendell Willkie avoided the war issue in the campaign. That he was roundly beaten by FDR seemed to prove the country was, at heart, pro-Ally.

The Willkie convention was televised; a first inkling of the decisive role that television would eventually play in politics. NBC

The Republican Convention of 1940 in Philadelphia, which nominated Wendell Willkie for the Presidency, was the first event of its kind to be telecast, though on a very limited basis.

The first baseball game ever televised was played between Princeton and Columbia at Baker Field, New York City, on May 17, 1939, and broadcast by NBC. Bill Stern was the announcer.

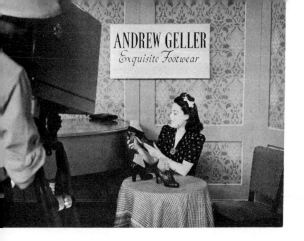

On July 1, 1941, the Federal Communications Commission gave television the green light for commercial operation. This photo shows one of four commercials telecast over NBC and CBS on the first day.

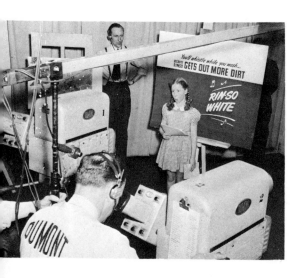

Commercials in the Forties were far removed from the mini-plays they became in the Sixties.

unveiled a 507-line picture, producing an image almost as clear and well-defined as the one we receive today. The pioneer coaxial cable carried the program to New York for re-broadcast. Television was gaining in stature among those aware of it. The Federal Communications Commission, established by Congress in 1934 mainly to regulate the air-waves, was scratching its head.

In February, members of the FCC attended an impressive demonstration at W2XB, Schenectady. They saw a telecast from New York, some 130 miles away, as received by a General Electric relay antenna on four 128-foot towers. In Wisconsin, the *Milwaukee Journal* filed the first application to broadcast television commercially. But the FCC was undecided. It questioned whether television was ready for general use. Several different systems were in operation, meaning that different types of receivers were required. The FCC felt it necessary to standardize the manufacture of television sets, which in turn meant a standard for transmission. Also involved was frequency modulation (FM) high-fidelity radio, made practical by the inventions of Edwin Armstrong in 1933. FM competed with TV for what was left of available frequencies after AM long-wave and short-wave radio were accommodated.

The FCC finally settled these matters in 1941, issuing official standards for the industry which, incidentally, placed TV sound transmission on FM. By that time the nation was on the brink of war. Development of both new media would be frozen for the duration. Before the boom was lowered, however, television kept prying into new areas of programming like an inquisitive child. A format took shape in this brief period that with modifications persists to this day.

There were only about 7,000 sets in operation in the New York area, with a smaller number clustered around a few other cities with transmitters. (Television signals do not carry as far as radio, because they penetrate the Heaviside layer in the atmosphere instead of bouncing off.) In 1940 this elite group of listeners saw the first televised basketball game (University of Pittsburgh 50, Fordham 37), the first hockey game (New York Rangers 6, Montreal Canadiens 2), the first opera (a condensed version of *Pagliacci* from an NBC studio), and the first circus (the complete three-hour show from Madison Square Garden). In March 1940, NBC put a portable transmitter aboard a United Air Lines transport, which flew over New York City at 2,000 feet to tele-see such sights as the Statue of Liberty, World's Fair Grounds, Grant's Tomb, and the Empire State Building.

The election returns of 1940 were televised from an NBC auditorium improvised into a newsroom, with invited guests. Viewers saw the news tickers tapping out reports, and shared the excitement of reporters rushing about while commentators explained the flow of votes from country-wide precincts. Color TV was publicly previewed by both RCA and CBS, using different systems. On September 3, 1940, Columbia's W2XAB showed members of the press the first high definition electronically scanned color broadcast. Using apparatus developed by Dr. Peter Clark Goldmark, CBS chief television engineer, it had a 343-line quality in black and white. A color disc placed in front of the receiver enabled the audience to view the pictures in color. But the technical problem of "compatabiiity," that is, whether color broadcasts could also be received in black and white by ordinary, non-color sets, was to keep TV's peacock out of the public eye for years to come.

On July 1, 1941, commercial television became a reality with the licensing of the first two transmitters, WNBT (NBC) and WCBW (CBS) in New York. They were required to offer four hours a week of regular programming, but actually presented about fifteen hours. One program that gave the motion picture industry a moment to stop and think was a prize fight, televised from Madison Square Garden and thrown onto a 15 x 20 foot theatre screen. Unfortunately it was a dull fight between two forgotten contestants, but the audience definitely saw every punch, every feint or bit of footwork, as clearly as observers at ringside.

World War II

The "day that will live in infamy," December 7, 1941, was a milestone for radio but very nearly a gravestone for television. The news of Pearl Harbor, cutting into calm Sunday afternoon radio programs such as the New York Philharmonic Symphony concert, rocked America back on its heels. Overnight only the war came to matter, civilian pursuits became unimportant. Television was a minor casualty. CBS presented a 90-minute television documentary of the Japanese attack—another forerunner of standard fare to come—but within a few weeks regular programming would be cut back to almost nothing. Many who worked in the new industry, a

Theater television was demonstrated by RCA at the New Yorker Theater in May 1941. Scenes from the Soose-Overlin middleweight championship fight at Madison Square Garden were projected on a 15 x 20 foot screen. In later years boxing championships were blacked out of free television channels so that tickets could be sold at theaters receiving the telecast by closed circuit.

Operas specially staged for television were providing regular fare for tube watchers of mid-Forties.

Dr. Peter Clark Goldmark in 1935, when he joined CBS as chief television engineer. A few years later he demonstrated the first high definition electronically scanned color TV system in a broadcast from the Chrysler Building in New York.

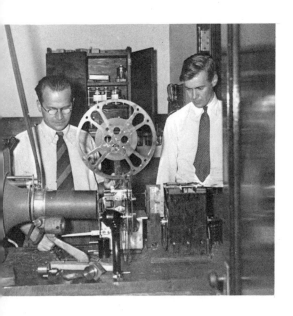

The CBS color sequential system of 1940 used a "dissector" camera and movie projector to broadcast color film. Shown inspecting it are Peter Goldmark and John Dyer, CBS engineers. It utilized Dr. Goldmark's film scanner with transmitted motion pictures without distortion or loss of definition.

mere infant at best, were called up for military service or shuttled into the production of war equipment. The nation needed radar for combatting the enemy, not images cavorting on a screen to amuse people at home. Scientists, technicians, producers, performers went into uniform, or to Deal, New Jersey, or Oak Ridge, Tennessee, and other secret centers of technology at war. Manufacture of TV sets stopped almost entirely.

But then, in 1942, still another future possibility began to peek over the wall when NBC began a TV training program for air-raid wardens—the first well-organized attempt at educational television. And TV entertainment found a new public to indoctrinate when major sports and variety programs were beamed to wounded servicemen in hospitals. Only one public station continued to operate throughout the war. This was the DuMont network, which began broadcasting out of New York on June 28, 1942, and received a commercial license as station WABD the following year. Stoutly resisting the trend, WABD broadcast programs featuring such stars as Dick Haymes, Henry Morgan, Paul Winchell and Jerry Mahoney, Luise Rainer, and Fred Waring's glee club.

One event of 1943 would have an important effect on television after the war. NBC sold the Blue Network and its key station, WJZ, to Edward J. Noble. This marked the birth of the American Broadcasting Company (ABC) which, ten years later, merged with United Paramount Theatres and became a third power in national network television.

While radio thrived, bringing news, entertainment, and "morale-building" programs to a populace working around the clock to supply American military forces, television only fitfully emerged from its deep sleep. Thus in 1943 station WRGB, Schenectady, televised the first complete opera, Humperdinck's *Hansel and Gretel*. The first telecast of an original movie short, entitled *Patrolling the Ether*, was transmitted simultaneously by three stations on April 10, 1944. They were WNBT, New York, and WPTZ, Philadelphia, besides WRGB. The "sponsor" was the FCC, whose wartime intelligence work in tracing illegal or espionage radio transmitters was portrayed in the film.

On September 28, *Esquire* magazine sponsored and broadcast over WABD, New York, the first musical comedy especially written for television, entitled *The Boys From Boise*.

The CBS television control panel in 1941 consisted of this battery of monitor screens and switches. Program director Tony Miner guided the act by telephone to the studio floor while his crew kept their hands at the ready to select the images which were to appear on television receivers.

Early in World War II, NBC television covered military maneuvers for the home screen. The helmets of First World War vintage identify this 1943 gun crew as a home defense unit.

By 1945 wartime restrictions had curtailed both NBC and CBS television programming to four hours a week. NBC's station, WWZ, was used to instruct air raid wardens in safety procedures.

News of the German surrender in 1945 brought an outpouring of celebrants to New York's Times Square, and television cameras to the marquee of the Hotel Astor.

Scientists and engineers continued tinkering with television hardware. Zworykin now had an "image-orthicon" tube, much more sensitive to light than earlier cathode-ray cameras. It meant that the devastating lights in television studios could be softened, protecting performers from the enervating effects of heat. Clearer pictures could be taken in natural light, indoors or out, with much improved reception. RCA also experimented with three-dimensional color TV for live talent, and with a projection-type receiver that increased the screen size to 24 inches wide. CBS opened its facilities to network clients for testing and developing commercial video programs.

President Harry S. Truman made his first network telecast at a Navy Day celebration in Central Park, New York, in 1945. The program was sent by cable to stations in Schenectady and Philadelphia. As company policy, NBC now was committed to a nationwide TV network. A possible way of extending the range was demonstrated in 1946 by RCA in cooperation with the Government, when a signal was relayed by an airplane in flight in the stratosphere.

During the next two years, "stratovision" improved to the point where on June 23, 1948, a telecast of the Republican National Convention in Philadelphia was picked up by a plane flying at 25,000 feet over Pittsburgh. It re-broadcast the program to a nine-state area of 525 miles diameter. In the fall, the sixth game of the World Series in Boston between the Braves and the Cleveland Indians was similarly "stratovised."

The end of the war was marked for television by a broadcast of the opening session of the United Nations Security Council at Hunter College in New York City. Surveys found that TV listeners would stay tuned for hours of serious colloquy if the subject were important enough—and at that time the United Nations appeared to many as the only hope for a peaceful world. These surveys also uncovered an odd statistic. There were still only 7,000 television sets in homes around the New York metropolitan area, virtually unchanged since before the war. But while only a handful of the population had ever seen television, the word was spreading fast. Servicemen who had been exposed to it were returning home. Laboratories and factories went back to work. Television receivers conforming to FCC standards began to roll off assembly lines. The age of television as we know it today finally was born.

The First Big Shows

The early postwar TV sets were either very small—8- or 10-inch screens were about standard—or very expensive. When a used-car millionaire who called himself "Madman" Muntz entered the business with a set costing $10 an inch ($170 for a 17-inch screen), this product created a sensation. Manufacturers cheated a little; the advertised width usually was a diagonal across the screen, while rounded corners cut off all but the center for receiving sharp images. Nevertheless the simultaneity of television overrode all defects; when people could see things happening far away, they couldn't get over the wonder of it. With every new broadcast, television picked up steam.

Sports broadcasts, for example, moved television sets en masse into neighborhood taverns and bars. The World Series and the Louis-Walcott fight must have sold 100,000 sets between them. Announcement of a Theatre Guild play would cause non-drinkers to cluster in the home of the lucky neighbor who owned a set. The appearance of President Truman delivering his State of the Union message to the 80th Congress in 1947 led to countless conversations that began, "Did you see . . . ?" Doctors waxed enthusiastic over the first telecasting of a surgical operation, staged for a meeting of the American College of Surgeons at a New York

In 1948, after the end of wartime material shortages, the Government lifted the freeze on television station construction, and new stations were built in major market areas. The American Broadcasting Company entered the network picture with the gala opening of WJZ-TV as its New York outlet on August 10, 1948. The Palace Theater, one-time citadel of vaudeville headliners, provided a fitting symbol of the new era.

Milton Berle went on the air every Tuesday night beginning in 1948, as master of ceremonies of Texaco Star Theater, *and stayed there until 1956. His program literally swept the country and brought television into the big leagues in terms of popularity. Known as "Uncle Miltie" or "Mr. Television," Berle featured brash and raucous comedy with outlandish character parts for himself, such as this desert prospector, and lavish production numbers with guest stars.*

hotel. There seemed no limit to the public service and excitement that TV could engender.

In entertainment, radio still held the attention of the vast majority of the public, but television unquestionably was turning into a competitor. A few big-name performers in radio, especially those whose material would be helped by "sight gags" along with words, music, and sound effects, began to get their feet wet in the new medium. Among them in 1948 were Arthur Godfrey, who made his TV debut with *Talent Scouts,* and Ted Mack with his *Original Amateur Hour.* Both were shows that would naturally benefit, since radio could not effectively display dancers, acrobats, or pretty girls, while TV could. In the same class was Ed Sullivan's *Toast of the Town,* which at this writing has survived more than twenty years. The home audience multiplied rapidly. Television was ready for its first smash hit.

Milton Berle and Sid Caesar

It came on Tuesday, September 14, 1948, when Milton Berle made his debut as master of ceremonies on *The Texaco Star Theatre.* He called himself "Uncle Miltie," but in show business he became known as "Mr. Television," and with good reason. On Tuesday nights anyone owning a TV set could expect a lot of visitors; crowds gathered in front of appliance stores to watch Berle on a set in the window; and many of the visitors and the watchers bought their own sets after this exhilarating experience. Berle's shows featured brash, loud comedy, outlandish costumes and weird props, and first-rate guest stars such as Gracie Fields. His supporting cast included Sid Stone, the pitchman, whose catch-phrase, "I'll tell ya what I'm gonna do," swept the country. The show had no writers at first; Berle simply did his old nightclub and vaudeville routines, and his guests did theirs. On that first show were singer Pearl Bailey, ventriloquist Señor Wences, dialect comedians Smith & Dale, and dancer Bill (Bojangles) Robinson.

Berle's gags came as fast as bullets. His stock-in-trade was slapstick, one-line jokes, and monologues that were unsurpassed. Here are some examples of his topical humor:

"I want to tell you something. The Republicans are in terrible trouble. They're trying to find somebody to run for President, and if they listen to me, I have a perfect candidate—Marilyn Monroe.

She'll get plenty of votes up north, and she's got a solid south, and what she could do with the U.N.! The Russians would sit still and watch *her* walk out."

"You know, to tell the truth, Bing Crosby may be forced to retire for financial reasons. His last check came back—insufficient banks! He doesn't have to worry because he can always get into politics. The Republicans want him to run for Governor of Santa Anita—to run on the mutuel ticket."

Of Bishop Fulton J. Sheen, whose religious program appeared at the same time as *Texaco Star Theatre,* Berle said one night: "We both work for the same boss—Sky Chief." Fortunately, the Bishop had a good sense of humor.

Some of the financial figures are revealing. In 1948 Berle's budget for the entire one-hour show was $15,000, an amount which would hardly pay for a 10-second spot commercial today. He took a cut of $750 in his old radio salary, which had been $2,000 a week. After a second season as the nation's top TV attraction he was boosted to $6,000. Uncle Miltie's basic program remained on the air under various sponsors until 1956, while Berle himself has continued as a prominent TV star to the present day.

As sophisticated as Berle was raucous, Sid Caesar first exhibited his extraordinary range of comic talent in 1949 in the *Admiral Broadway Review,* later renamed *Your Show of Shows.* Produced by Max Liebman, this was in effect a complete new musical "revue" every week, lasting 90 minutes and lavish in presentation. It was to make stars not only of Caesar but of Imogene Coca, Carl Reiner, and Howard Morris, his partners in hilarious sketches, burlesques of current affairs, pantomimes, and satirical lampoons of motion pictures and operas.

Behind the scenes the pace was frantic. Gag-writer Mel Brooks (later a film producer) and the cast would huddle on the stage at rehearsals, start with an idea and improvise, laughing uproariously, until they had an act. The versatile Caesar could also play the saxophone, and was muscular enough to take strong-man parts.

Funny and successful as it was, the Sid Caesar show also struck an ominous note for the future of television comedy. It revealed the medium's savage appetite for fresh material; the creative strain was too much even for such brilliant people. When *Your Show of Shows* went off the air in 1954 and the team broke up, it had set

Your Show of Shows *started in 1949 as the* Admiral Broadway Revue *starring Sid Caesar. His partner for many hilarious sketches was Imogene Coca.*

a standard for originality and intelligent humor that has never been equalled since.

Those early hits also proved that television was not to be a mere offshoot of radio, but would strike out in its own directions. Many performers closely identified with the older medium never successfully made the transition; among them such "top bananas" as Ed Wynn, "The Perfect Fool." On the other hand, new names virtually unknown to radio headed for stardom as soon as the public could see them. Thus in June, 1948, a handsome young baritone singer teamed with an impish brat of a comedian made a guest appearance on *Toast of the Town*. Their names would quickly become world-famous: Dean Martin and Jerry Lewis.

TV personalities

It was typical of Ed Sullivan to "discover" Martin and Lewis for his opening show (which also included pianist Eugene List,

After a separation of several years, comedians Sid Caesar and Imogene Coca were brought together again in a situation comedy on ABC in 1957.

dancer Kathryn Lee, composers Richard Rodgers and Oscar Hammerstein 2nd, fight referee Ruby Goldstein, and half a dozen others). Not a performer himself (quite the opposite!), Sullivan was a former sports writer and Broadway columnist for the New York *Daily News*. He got into show business when the paper assigned him to promote a dance contest for their readers called the "Harvest Moon Ball." Sullivan took the winners on a vaudeville tour, and thus developed a special talent for pulling together a good show, sometimes out of little material, that has been his golden goose ever since.

Ed Sullivan, who first appeared on home screens in 1948 with his Toast of the Town, *gained undisputed command of Sunday nights by the mid-Fifties, and continued appearing weekly for 20 years. This 1956 picture illustrates the secret of his longevity: he selects performers of current interest and then steps aside to let them perform.*

While many of Sullivan's guests might be individually outstanding, what distinguished the show from the beginning was the personality of the M.C. himself. Awkward in manner and in speech, almost gun-shy in front of an audience, Sullivan nevertheless had a nose for news, novelty, and topical interest that made him a master showman. He would present sports heroes or famous entertainers exactly when they were in the public eye or likely to provoke controversy. Among them through the years were Elvis Presley, a "rock 'n' roll" singer given to pelvic gyrations then considered shocking; Ingrid Bergman at a moment when her private life was creating gossip; the Moiseyev folk dancers, who were controversial because they had been imported from Soviet Russia; and those teen-age terrors, the Beatles.

Sullivan knew variety talent when he saw it, whether trained dog acts or Metropolitan Opera singers; and he had a way of getting off the stage and letting them do their turns without interference. This very unobtrusiveness in public, coupled with iron-willed dictatorial control of every production detail when *not* in public, helped the show to catch on slowly but soundly. The *Ed Sullivan Show* remained impregnable in listener attention every Sunday night, long after seemingly more vibrant stars had dropped from sight.

The advent of the female personality on TV came in 1949 with Faye Emerson, an urbane young actress with impressive social connections (she had been married to a son of President Roosevelt). Her technique was that of the interview, bringing interesting people before the camera from the worlds of entertainment, journalism, sports or politics. She also broke a barrier of propriety by appearing on television in low-cut gowns, causing a nationwide furore for a short time. When viewers realized that beauty was made to be seen

Dean Martin and Jerry Lewis when they first gained recognition as a comedy team on TV and in the movies. They made their television debut on Ed Sullivan's Toast of the Town *in 1948.*

Alfred Hitchcock, the brilliant English film director, brought his formidable talents to television in 1955 with the suspense show, Alfred Hitchcock Presents. *Acting as host, he delivered wry monologues which almost—but not quite—gave the impression that crime does pay. Photo shows him, right, in an appearance on the Ed Sullivan show in 1957.*

as well as heard, they got used to it. Miss Emerson was the prototype for the Dorothy Kilgallens and Arlene Francises who have been a prominent feature of TV panel and talk shows ever since.

The eerie way in which the television camera makes or breaks a personality—sees right through him to pick up some quality that the audience either likes or doesn't—made Perry Como the first TV hit as a male pop singer, rather than radio's darlings such as Bing Crosby and Frank Sinatra. He first appeared in 1948 on *Chesterfield Supper Club,* quickly dominated it, and in two years made it his own show. A former barber from Canonsburg, Pennsylvania, Como had a relaxed style and a casual manner that came through the tube as "Mr. Nice Guy." His singing never won any prizes; it was his easy-going personality that endeared him to the viewer in the intimate atmosphere of everyone's living room. Como continued as a top-rated TV performer until well into the Sixties.

The FCC freeze

As these and other stars, along with increasingly agile and comprehensive coverage of news and sports, swiftly multiplied the audience for television, advertising money began to pour into the new medium in staggering amounts. Radio stations, newspapers, and other interests rushed to build transmitters and acquire lucrative TV licenses. Again the FCC had to scratch its head. In 1948, pending a study of the many rising problems, the Commission "froze" all new licensing. Operating transmitters were developing interferences which had not been anticipated. The public interest also seemed in jeopardy; the FCC was fearful of monopoly, or suspicious of the propaganda intentions of some of the applicants. It felt that both engineering and policy questions should be answered before any new stations were allowed on the air.

Not until April 1952 was the freeze lifted, along with a study and statement of principles that were to govern television operations for years to come. Among these were new engineering standards, consideration of color systems, the reservation of channels for non-commercial or educational TV, a definition of public service programming on commercial stations, and a national assignment plan for VHF and UHF channels.

The appearance of Elvis Presley on the Ed Sullivan show caused considerable controversy, because of the gyrations that accompanied his rock-and-roll singing. Sullivan ordered his cameramen to show Presley only from the waist up. Within a few years, however, both "Elvis the Pelvis" and his singing would be considered so tame as to be virtually decorous.

In 1948 Arthur Godfrey made his debut with Talent Scouts *and in 1949 he did* Arthur Godfrey and His Friends. *By the late fifties, Godfrey had become an elder statesman of American television. An entire generation had grown from birth to maturity with Godfrey's relaxed radio voice and ingratiating television smile, sometimes best exemplified by his highly personal method of handling commercials.*

Perry Como made his name on radio as a singer, as star of the Chesterfield Supper Club, *which shifted to television in 1948. Using the techniques of relaxed monologue or dialogue with a guest such as George Gobel, all interspersed with pleasant music, Como created an intimate, casual type of entertainment. With the help of the brilliant comedy writer, Goodman Ace, and his able staff, Mort Green, George Foster, and J. Burton,* The Perry Como Show *grew from a 15-minute spot in 1950 to an hour-long NBC Saturday night series that hit the top in ratings in 1955. Although Como gave up the weekly series in 1963, he continued as a top performer in several special shows a year.*

Color TV

Three competitive color systems were offered for FCC consideration in 1949. Two years earlier, in denying a formal petition by CBS, the Commission had urged further experimentation to make color transmission possible in the 6-megacycle band used by system, the RCA "dot sequential" system, and the "line sequential" system of Color Television, Inc. Each would require special receiving sets. However, the CBS color signals could not be received in black-and-white on existing receivers without adapters; the two others claimed they could.

This placed the FCC in a quandary. It favored the CBS system as the only one then presented that met its color criteria, but postponed decision until manufacturers would agree to equip all new TV sets with an adapter circuit for color reception. When the trade failed to respond to this appeal, the Commission on October 11, 1950, adopted the CBS system nevertheless. It left the door open to development of a better system on the basis of practical tests. RCA promptly obtained a federal court injunction, which delayed color transmission until overruled by the Supreme Court on May 28, 1951. Then, because of the Korean War and a materials shortage, the National Production Authority prohibited manufacture of color sets or adapters, and interest in the field sequential system lagged. Thereafter, the industry formed the National Television System Committee to develop new color standards. These were advocated to the FCC and finally adopted on December 17, 1953.

The present standards are based on the "simultaneous" system, which transmits three signals for three primary colors (red, green, and blue) at the same time. It is "compatible" in that all existing TV sets can receive the three signals and combine them into an acceptable black and white picture. Also, color sets can receive monochrome transmissions, combining the three colors emitted by the tube into a greenish-black image that resembles rotogravure printing.

Music on TV

On March 20, 1948, Arturo Toscanini conducted the NBC Symphony Orchestra in an all-Wagnerian program. A television audience of nearly 400,000 watched, fascinated, as the camera concentrated on the expressive hand and facial movements of the famous conductor, or moved with the music from the strings to the woodwinds, brasses, and tympani. In November Verdi's *Otello* was telecast, complete, from the Metropolitan Opera House for three and a half hours, sponsored by Texaco. A year later Leonard Bernstein made his TV debut with the Boston Symphony in a special program for the United Nations.

By 1949 a regular rating system had been set up to determine the popular programs of the year. Milton Berle was way out in front in thirty cities, but programs of serious music were also among the tops in popularity. Eventually, though, for a curious reason, this lively interest in symphony and opera would benefit FM radio rather than TV. Television sound is transmitted via static-free FM, but most sets are equipped with only minimum audio circuits and tiny speakers (in order to hold down the price). Sound reception is merely adequate, not good enough for the music aficionado. In later years some stations would try to overcome this defect by "simulcasting" concerts on TV and FM stereo bands; the listener could watch the performance (without sound) on the tube and simultaneously hear the music (without sight) on his separate hi-fi radio speakers.

Horses and guns

The Western action story came thundering across television screens in 1948 through the business sagacity of William Boyd. Once a star of Cecil B. De Mille's *King of Kings, The Volga Boatmen,* and other epics, the film actor for years had been grinding out low-budget "B" pictures based on the *Hopalong Cassidy* stories. He had the amazing foresight to buy the television rights, at a time when feature films were generally being barred from telecasting by the major Hollywood companies. The simple-minded horse operas, hardly ever seen in movie theatres except on Saturday mornings, became an overnight sensation on the home screen. Boyd made a fortune from endlessly repeated showings of his 100 films, plus the royalties from sales of "Hoppy" hats and cowboy clothes to a generation of children.

Another movie cowboy, Gene Autry, who sang between tosses of his lariat and cracks of his six-gun, made films especially for

One of the first female TV personalities, Faye Emerson caused a furore for a short time by wearing low-cut gowns on camera.

William Boyd became one of the first and most popular television cowboys with the repeated showings of his western movies.

Gertrude Berg as Mollie Goldberg, author and star of The Rise of the Goldbergs, *one of the earliest family situation comedy successes on television.*

television beginning in 1947. When *The Lone Ranger* came over from radio the following year, the flood was on in earnest. For years the mingled sounds of pistol shots, hooves, and cries of "He went thataway!" from a dozen Western series would identify every American household that boasted both a TV set and kids. Along with its audience the Western grew into adulthood and became the television rage of the Fifties.

Guns without horses got their television start in *Martin Kane, Private Eye,* which went on the air in 1949. This earliest of successful cops-and-robbers series was blessed with fine actors in the part of the indomitable, incorruptible private detective. During its five-year run they were successively Lee Tracy, Lloyd Nolan, William Gargan, and Mark Stevens. Like the Westerns, crime-action-spy stories on TV grew up and began to invade prime evening hours. They also set a precedent for TV fare in general: *repetition* of the same characters, as in a newspaper comic strip, kept the audience coming back for more.

Family situation stories

In these early years of television, the basic appeal of the medium—believability—was reflected in the entertainment offered for adults. *The Goldbergs,* a classic on radio, moved to TV in 1949. It had the warm humor and insight into human relations that Gertrude Berg, who both wrote the script and played the part of Mollie, infused into her gentle tales of a Jewish family in the Bronx. A similar appeal with different ethnic backgrounds made successes of *Mama* and *Life with Luigi* in the same period. The first, based on the novel and play, *I Remember Mama,* depicted the trials and joys of a Scandinavian family in the Midwest. "Luigi" was an Italian immigrant in Chicago, played by J. Carrol Naish of the inimitable accent. Alan Reed was Pasquale, his friend with the un-marriageable daughter Rosa.

The uncomfortable realism of television eventually proved fatal to the ethnic humor that had first blossomed on radio. *Amos 'n' Andy,* for example, which moved to TV in 1951, would perish in the Sixties before the onslaughts of civil-rights groups who protested that it was a caricature of Negro life. A more permanent pattern was discernible in 1949 in *The Life of Reilly,* starring Jackie Gleason (later William Bendix). The lovable bumbler gradually turned into a wild distortion of American fatherhood, so abysmally stupid as to enter the realm of fantasy. So long as no ethnic or other toes were stepped on, no one's oxen gored, television writers began to find that they could strain credibility to the breaking point.

Major television drama

Live theatre equivalent to the Broadway stage, the subject of many early experiments, came to television on a regular, commercially sponsored basis on May 7, 1947, with the premiere of *Kraft Television Theatre.* The one-hour show was *Double Door,* an original drama starring John Baragrey in a cast of five. The series ran two nights a week on two networks, NBC and ABC, during the first year, and beginning in 1949 was carried to the Midwest by coaxial cable. In its long career "Theatre" telecast some 650 plays, both originals and adaptations of Broadway productions. Rod Serling was one of its outstanding playwrights.

The first dramas originated in the cramped confines of a radio studio, with a minimum of background changes and props. But the field was wide open for experimentation. Young producers, directors, actors, and actresses eagerly moved in with new ideas for using the amazing capabilities (and overcoming the severe limitations) of the new medium.

Among them was Fred Coe, producer of *Television Playhouse* for Philco, Goodyear, and other sponsors. This Sunday night NBC series began October 3, 1948, and ran well into the Fifties with some of the finest legitimate theatre ever seen on the air. Coe sought excitement in new talents and original plays. He looked for young writers, and encouraged them to write their own kind of dramas, which he interspersed with first-rate productions of the classics. It is this series, recalled for the youthful output of such playwrights as Paddy Chayefsky, Tad Mosel, Robert Alan Aurthur, Gore Vidal, and others, that many regard as the beginning of television's most creative period.

For CBS, another fine producer, Worthington Miner, began telecasting *Studio One* on Monday night, November 7, 1948, with Margaret Sullavan in *The Storm.* His technique differed from Coe's; he concentrated on the image rather than the words. Miner's pro-

William Bendix as Riley and Henry Kulky as Otto Schmidlapp in a 1955 episode from The Life of Riley. *This situation comedy, first shown in 1949 and revived (with Bendix) in 1953, was the prototype of a TV genre which has been described as "artificial characters in artificial situations being egged on by artificial laughter."*

ductions were featured by unusual camera angles, bold innovations, lifelike visual techniques. He did many TV versions of famous stage plays, as well as distinguished originals such as several works by Reginald Rose.

On a more mundane level, the daytime "true-to-life" serial moved over from radio in 1949 with *One Man's Family.* Its cast included Bert Lytell and Eva-Marie Saint. This, too, set a pattern. The serials were never to depart too far from a semblance of reality, and the acting in them would continue to be of superior quality. It had to be; the "soap opera" was necessarily a quickie, turned out five times a week with a minimum of rehearsal time. Only the most expert of actors and actresses could pick up their lines and the story's mood so fast. In fact, when a performer was obliged to leave the company temporarily or permanently, the script writer would obligingly recast the story to account for his absence.

All of these early productions were strictly live (even when a successful show was repeated on the air); the era of filming and taping was several years ahead. Many still regret the loss of the fresh "first night" feeling of the live shows; and it is true that TV, essentially a projection of real life, loses something (including unexpected fluffs) when slicked up for filming. The actors, however, do not regret it. Governor Ronald Reagan, who played and hosted for eight years in *GE Theater* both live and filmed, described the difference in his 1965 campaign biography, *Where's The Rest of Me?* written with Richard G. Hubler:

> Eventually we went to all film for the simple reason that film gave better quality in every way . . . In our live efforts, the various sets are built around the perimeter of the studio with three mobile cameras, sound equipment, etc., maneuvering in the cleared central area. One scene might end with a character obliged to run from one end of the studio to a set at the other end, peeling off a coat and tugging on another, to indicate (by costume change) a lapse of time. Watch those live shows—the pants don't change. This is what made for the slower pace; very often one camera would focus on a steaming cup of coffee, or the curling smoke from a cigarette on an ashtray. Twenty seconds would be wasted on this scenic nothing, while actors scrambled into a new getup. In film, on the other hand, you simply snip the film and glue it onto the next scene.

I could never quite keep my sense of humor when actors who should have known better would argue that live TV was more like the stage, in that you could sustain an emotion . . . Nancy [his wife] and I did a live half-hour for GE and she played the first ten minutes wearing two dresses. At one point she left a romantic scene with me, running like crazy for another set, while a wardrobe woman unzipped and removed the outer dress (pull one zipper too many and we'd be off the air). Her next scene called for her to be worried to the point of distraction. Now, what emotion did she sustain?

What those performers really meant was that they got to a high, nervous, keyed-up pitch making all these mechanical didoes work without a foul-up, while acting at the same time . . . and they got a real happy reaction when the little red lights clicked off and they knew they'd made it. But we aren't supposed to be in this business for our own kicks, and the audience doesn't really care how we manage the backstage tricks: they want to see the play without the seams showing.

Jack Barry, half of the ingenious Barry and Enright team of program producers, appeared in many of his own shows. His Juvenile Jury, first telecast in 1947, used children as panelists who advised their contemporaries on "perplexing personal problems." This 1954 panel included Joe Ward, Michele Fogel, and Douglas Stewart.

Barry later hosted another children's program, Winky-Dink and You, in the Fifties, and two of the big money quiz shows, Twenty-One and Tic-Tac-Dough.

Paul Tripp brought Mr. I. Magination *to television in 1949, creating a magical town where any child's wishes would come true. It is interesting and a bit sad to speculate how and why this innocent type of entertainment came to be displaced by horror stories for children during the next ten years.*

Winky Dink and You encouraged participation of children at home by distributing coloring books, games, etc., to listeners through the mail. Host Jack Barry then guided the game or story on the air with a member of the live audience.

The very earliest experimenters in television, and the earliest owners of receiving sets, discovered immediately that kids could scarcely be horsewhipped away from it. Children were completely, uncritically fascinated, seemingly insatiable in their appetite for almost any sort of entertainment. They were also impressionable consumers of goods. Programs for children were among the first full-fledged hits, beginning with *Howdy Doody* in 1947. Buffalo Bob Smith was a puppeteer and ventriloquist who built a lively show around the puppet (Howdy Doody) and a clown named Clarabell. The content was complete, corny nonsense, punctuated by the wild screams of a cheering section composed of small girls and boys.

Parents complained at the absence of any "educational" value; and this argument about what children's TV programs ought to be has continued ever since; but the same parents practically clawed and scratched their way into the studio to get tickets to the live telecast for their children. Other programs of the late Forties for

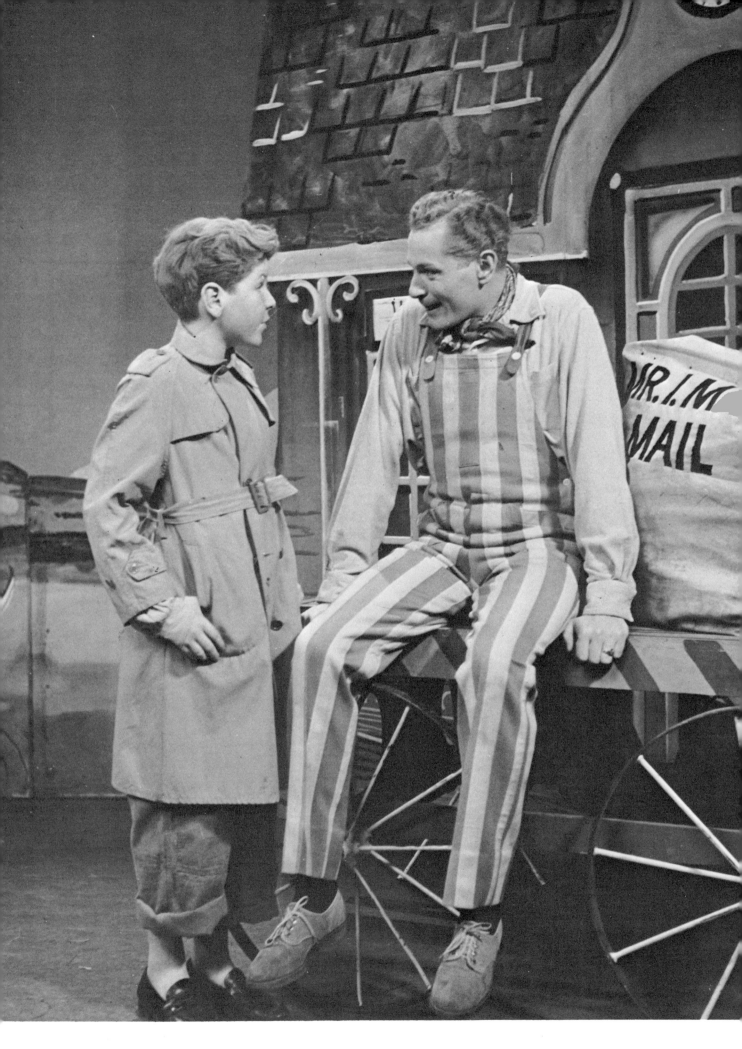

Setting a pattern for puppet popularity, Kukla, Fran and Ollie originated as a local show in Chicago and soared to network success in 1949. Burr Tillstrom was the puppeteer, Fran Allison the "live" member of the Kuklapolitan troupe. Intended for children, the gentle whimsey of the patter also charmed a large adult following.

the tots, such as *Kukla, Fran and Ollie* and *Mr. I Magination*, may be recalled more fondly by adults, but none ever reached the heights of hysterical fandom that "Howdy" did. And none, apparently, was equally successful in inducing children to tell Mommy to "buy me this."

Among the top twenty shows as the decade drew to a close were Milton Berle, *Fireside Theatre*, *Philco TV Playhouse*, *Stop the Music* (taken from radio), *Cavalcade of Stars*, *We, The People* (also from radio), *Small Fry Club,* and *Fireball Fun For All*. High in popularity were *Kraft Television Theatre*, *On Broadway*, *Americana*, *NBC Symphony,* and Walter Winchell. Television was entering upon its Golden Age, without question beginning to sweep into and influence every phase of American life.

No children's show before or since has achieved the hysterical following of Howdy Doody, *which had been on the air ten years when this picture was taken. The "peanut gallery" of youngsters screamed their appreciation of former disk jockey Buffalo Bob Smith, puppet Howdy, and clown Clarabell, whose voice was an auto horn.*

4. Golden Age: The Fifties

The dawn of the second half of the twentieth century aroused none of the hysterical enthusiasm of 1900. A treasured set of values had perished with World War II, and in 1950 America was just becoming uncomfortably aware of it. The atomic bomb, first exploded in 1945; the emergence of the U.S.A. and the U.S.S.R. as super-powers confronting one another in Berlin, southern Europe, and Asia; the Communist takeover of China . . . all these were cause for uneasiness and insecurity. President Truman, manfully facing crisis after crisis, had surprisingly won reelection in 1948, but when the cold war turned hot in Korea his popularity rapidly ebbed. Americans were suddenly weary of playing Atlas with an explosive world on their backs. A decade of consolidation, of turning inward, lay ahead.

The 1952 presidential election confirmed the change of heart. General Dwight D. Eisenhower, the father image, promising "I shall go to Korea," crushingly defeated a master of words, Governor Adlai E. Stevenson of Illinois. Spy exposures deepened American distrust and suspicion of the rest of the world, encouraging Senator Joseph McCarthy of Wisconsin to make political capital of finding spies inside every Government desk. But the domestic economy entered a period of expansion and prosperity that would continue with only minor interruptions for more than fifteen years. The young people of the Fifties would become known to liberal reformers as the Silent Generation, but to conservative businessmen as the Practical Generation, intent on achieving affluence and devil take the philosophers. One of the boom industries was television. In 1950 the picture tube definitely overtook radio as the medium of total entertainment in the habits of the American people. The Image forged ahead of The Word.

As if to prove it, Tallulah Bankhead attempted to recapture the radio audience with her lavish, star-studded Sunday night program, *The Big Show,* on NBC radio. It didn't last. The Nielsen ratings, which had taken over from Hooper, at first showed a lingering mass audience for radio shows, but by the end of 1950 the switch to TV was in full flood. As of January 1, 1946, there had been only about 10,000 TV sets in the entire United States. On April 1, 1951, five years and a few months later, 12,000,000 sets

An NBC television camera covering a session of the United Nations in New York in 1950. TV had been present at the opening session of the organization in 1946, and continued to record its more important debates.

Television's first "hot" war was the Korean conflict that began in 1950. Here a CBS remote pickup unit covers distant combat action with a telescopic lens.

69

In the Fifties, mobile television units began to bring swift news and live pictures to the viewer. Here the aftermath of a 1955 flood in California.

were operating throughout the country. What radio had pioneered in the organizing of technical and creative talents, in the administrative structure of a totally new business in America, television now absorbed with a style and flair of its own. The picture tube eventually would force the sound medium to think up new ways of making itself heard.

The fast-growing television public began to see radio, stage, and screen stars in bigger and more elaborate programs. To Berle and Caesar were added Groucho Marx, Ken Murray, Eddie Cantor, Sam Levenson, Garry Moore—these in 1950 alone. Red Skelton, Bob Hope, Jack Benny, Jimmy Durante, Martha Raye, Dinah Shore, Phil Silvers, Fred Allen, George Gobel, and Danny Thomas

Grand Old Opry and its captivating mixture of country-and-western music made its TV debut in 1952. One of its most popular performers was earthy Minnie Pearl, shown in a scene with Marty Robbins in 1958.

all plunged into the new medium and their shows quickly caught on with the public. Groucho was the host of *You Bet Your Life,* a half-hour quiz. In the same year another combination of jest and contest, *What's My Line?,* got under way. John Daly, as moderator, and Arlene Francis, one of the four original panel members in 1950, would remain on the show until its switch to daytime hours in 1968.

In 1951, Jackie Gleason made television history by introducing "The Honeymooners," a series of husband-and-wife comedy sketches, on *Cavalcade of Stars.* Later, on *The Jackie Gleason Show,* the series attained enormous popularity. Gleason, a creative comedian with an eye for character and an ear for the common speech, played Ralph the bus driver, with the talented Art Carney as his neighbor, the sewer worker, and Audrey Meadows as his wife Alice. In the mid-Fifties Gleason received one of the biggest contracts in television history—a $7 million deal. Reruns of "The Honeymooners" continued to rate high in popularity more than 10 years later.

An example of Gleason humor:

Alice: "Look Ralph, maybe until you get something for yourself, I could get a job to help out."

Gleason: "Oh no you don't. When I married you I promised you'd never have to work again."

Alice: "But it won't be for long."

Gleason: "I don't care, Alice. I've got my pride. Before I'd let you go to work, I'd rather see you starve. We'll just have to live on our savings."

Alice: "That'll carry us through the night, but what'll we do in the morning?"

The original New York-Philadelphia coaxial cable now extended westward, creeping toward the Pacific Coast like the transcontinental rails for the Iron Horse in the previous century. Television antennas were sprouting from every rooftop in its wake. In Hollywood, a few far-sighted movie makers began to see the handwriting on the wall. The waggish Samuel Goldwyn is said to have asked, "Why should anyone pay to see a bad picture in a theater when he can see one for nothing at home?" He suggested forming a posse to halt the advance of the coaxial cable in the Utah desert. On September 4, 1951, with the cable completed, NBC began coast-to-coast operations with 61 stations.

At first the motion picture Goliath tried to ignore the upstart young David. Recent films were not for sale to TV. So the net-

Dinah Shore as a golden-voiced thrush attained instant popularity in 1954, the only female vocalist able to sustain her own weekly musical show. She did it with patter, gowns, and guests.

Jackie Gleason has appeared on television almost continually since 1950. In the series The Honeymooners, *he played a bus driver living in New York. Audrey Meadows was his wife, Alice, and Art Carney, their neighbor, Norton. Carney, a Gleason discovery, became famous overnight with the advent of this series.*

Later, in a weekly variety series, Gleason showed the depth of his talent by portraying four radically different characters. Here (pictured with Art Carney), he is Reginald Van Gleason III.

Jackie Gleason helped reunite the musical Dorsey brothers after they had parted company. He is shown here on one of his programs with Tommy (left) and Jimmy Dorsey.

In 1950, as an established radio "name," Garry Moore switched to television with a daily afternoon show. He reduced the grind to three times a week in 1954, and abandoned it in 1958 saying, "I'm tired." Shortly after, the Garry Moore Show reappeared as a once-a-week nighttime program that continued until 1964. Moore also hosted game and quiz shows.

Moore's show was the vehicle to stardom for an unknown comedienne, Carol Burnett. She appears here in a crazy episode with her able foil Durwood Kirby.

works combed film libraries for old pictures, even silent ones, those independently owned, animated cartoons, and foreign imports. Laurel and Hardy, for example, made a hit all over again with a new generation of American children. English, French, and especially Italian films made stars of foreign players through TV exposure in the United States. On the creative side, the imports completely changed the concept of what constitutes "adult" entertainment. With the hot breath of the newcomer breathing down the neck of the giant, tremors of doubt and frustration rolled throughout the film industry.

An early switch-over from radio (1949) was It Pays To Be Ignorant, a quiz show in which the less a "contestant" knew, the better. Playing it for laughs were quizmaster Tom Howard (left) supported by George Shelton, Lulu Mc-Connell, and Harry McNaughton.

Perhaps television's greatest funny man, Red Skelton, has brightened the lives of viewers since 1953. Here, he spoofs the Western drama with Pat O'Brien.

What's My Line? was the pioneer panel show, first going on the air in 1950 and continuing until 1968. For most of those years the panelists were Arlene Francis (left), Dorothy Kilgallen, and publisher Bennett Cerf, with John Daly as quiz-master. The fourth panelist, Ernie Kovacs in this 1957 picture, was changed from week to week. Its producers, Goodson-Todman, used a similar formula in several other panel shows.

Definitely, television had become a habit, almost an addiction. People were staying home from the movies. Receipts were tumbling. Movie houses all over the country closed their doors and opened again as supermarkets. The very structure that had created the mammoth studio control over its star system was headed for collapse. While eventually the "war" between the rival industries was called off, and Hollywood began making or releasing films for television, one long-range result was a complete change in the fare shown at cinema theaters. The wide screen—Cinemascope, Todd A-O, Vista-Vision, 3-D—appeared. On it played Technicolor

MR. KOVACS   MISS KILGALLEN   MR. CERF

spectacles and epics, along with features considered too sophisticated, risqué, or esoteric for the family audience now surrendered to the home screen.

On television now, innovations tumbled over one another to exploit every shade of audience interest. Some were pretty ridiculous (e.g., the roller derby, wrestling, or that Latin lover, *The Continental*), but some made history. We may briefly highlight particular programs that established the Fifties as the new medium's Golden Age of creativity or significance, or both.

This Is Show Business invited guest performers to display their talents and submit their problems to a group of wits for discussion and solution. In this 1952 program Jack Benny (second from left) aired his ambitions as a violinist for panelists Sam Levenson, George S. Kaufman, and Clifton Fadiman.

Kefauver, Murrow, and McCarthy

Masquerade Party was a game show which lent itself well to television visual techniques and frankly played the game for laughs. The panelists attempted to guess the identity of celebrities wearing bizarre and confusing costumes—Peter Donald (right) was host.

In 1951 television more or less accidentally discovered that real life—watched on the tube—could be both stranger and more electrifying than planned entertainment. Senator Estes Kefauver of Tennessee, head of a committee investigating crime in America, permitted the Senate hearings to be broadcast live. Huge TV audiences watched, fascinated, as committee counsel Rudolph Halley mercilessly quizzed such exotic figures as Virginia Hill, the gangster's girl friend, and gambler Frank Costello. Costello insisted that

PHIL SILVERS   BUFF COBB   OGDEN NASH   ILKA CHASE

Intellectual television games were popular in 1955. Dr. Bergen Evans of Northwestern University moderated several shows, including Down You Go, which was based on the correct definitions and use of words. Standing are Patricia Cutts, Fran Coughlin, and Phyllis Cerf.

To Tell the Truth *was another* Goodson-Todman *package with* Bud Collyer *as m.c. and panelists* Polly Bergen, Hume Cronyn, Hildy Parks *and* Dick Van Dyke.

his face could not be shown, but the camera focused on his hands performing an unforgettable nervous ballet. The consequences of the telecast were even more extraordinary.

Senator Kefauver, having sold his story of the crime exposures for a large sum to the *Saturday Evening Post*, invested the proceeds in a campaign for the Democratic nomination for president in 1952. His technique was to go directly to the people in state primary elections, which professional politicians had ignored for half a century. (President Truman called presidential primaries "bunk.") Although he did not succeed in winning the nomination, Kefauver won enough committed delegates to establish the primaries as a key proving ground for all future presidential conven-

Captain Kangaroo (Bob Keeshan) was a graduate of Howdy Doody *where he played the clown. In entertaining pre-school children the Captain used gentle fantasy, quiet talk, and even educational material, pleasing parents and educators as well as the youngsters. The show has topped its field since 1955.*

The late Walt Disney, Hollywood's authentic genius of the animat[ed] cartoon, nature-adventure film, American history, and fairy tales f[or] children that also delighted adults, introduced all of them to televisi[on] on his Disneyland *show for ABC in 1954.*

Edward R. Murrow introduced his famous See It Now *series in 1951 by showing a "live" view of the Atlantic Ocean followed by a view of the Pacific Ocean. He said, "We are impressed by a medium in which a man sitting in his living room has been able for the first time to look at two oceans at once." In the years that followed, Murrow roamed the world for his television viewers. During the Suez crisis and war in 1956, he interviewed an Israeli sheepherder whose flock was stolen near the Syrian border.*

Grandma Moses was one of a number of artists and other talented people whom Murrow deemed significant material for See It Now. *The cameraman is Leo Rossi.*

tions. In 1960, Senator John F. Kennedy would ride this route to victory. But the victory actually was television's. When viewers could watch history being made right before their eyes, the Image involved the American people in public affairs more directly than ever before, including millions who scarcely ever read a newspaper.

The earliest television newscasters, such as John Cameron Swayze (1947) and Douglas Edwards (1948), recited news dispatches much as they had done on radio. In 1951 the late Edward R. Murrow took a giant step forward with *See It Now;* he combined film footage and live commentary into a new form, the television documentary. It had the vividness of movie newsreels with the immediacy of a radio bulletin, imbued with a dignity and integrity that set a high standard for all who followed. Murrow and his producer, Fred W. Friendly, roamed the wide world for stories of significance and consequence, not hesitating to tackle controversial issues. In 1954, with the remark "This is no time for men who oppose Senator Joseph R. McCarthy's methods to keep silent," Murrow on *See It Now* launched a scathing exposé of a man most commentators were afraid to touch. When CBS gave McCarthy equal time to reply, the Senator attempted on Murrow the same technique of character assassination that Murrow had just criticized.

The episode marked the beginning of McCarthy's end as a sinister force in American politics. Within the year, the U. S. Department of the Army, bedeviled by McCarthy's charge that "Communist" officers were being promoted, decided to fight back. The televised hearings before a Senate committee, in effect a trial of McCarthy for veracity, made high drama and political history. Prompted by the Army's defense counsel, Joseph N. Welch of Boston, the cathode tube bored mercilessly into the character of the witnesses. When, in one unforgettable confrontation, the mild-mannered Welch cried out, "Have you no sense of decency, sir? At long last, have you no sense of decency?" McCarthy was finished. He was to endure formal censure by the Senate (after hearings also televised) before his death a year later.

The spectaculars

On Christmas Eve, 1951, NBC boldly invaded a sacrosanct cultural domain: the opera. It was Gian-Carlo Menotti's *Amahl and the Night Visitors,* specifically written for television. Those who saw and heard this totally charming Nativity play, set to original music,

"The Secret Life of Danny Kaye" was a 1957 See It Now show that revealed the comedian visiting children all over the world as the good-will ambassador of UNICEF. He is seen here in Nigeria demonstrating that comedy knows no insurmountable language, racial, or cultural barriers.

Edward R. Murrow interviewing the U.A.R. (Egyptian) chief of state, President Nasser, in 1957.

Gian-Carlo Menotti's opera Amahl and the Night Visitors, *written exclusively for television, went on the air on Christmas Eve, 1951 and has been a Yuletide fixture ever since. The cast from the 1966 version comprises (from left) Willis Patterson, John McCollum, Richard Cross, Martha King, and Kurt Yaghjian as the crippled shepherd boy, Amahl, in the miracle scene.*

Tchaikovsky's "Nutcracker" ballet, a 1957 Christmas show on CBS's The Seven Lively Arts, danced by the New York City Ballet, became a perennial attraction.

felt they were witnessing the birth of a new tradition. They were correct in a sense; while television did not proceed to other operas, other triumphs of musical drama, *Amahl* itself became a perennial. The original boy soprano, Chet Allen, outgrew his part, but Rosemary Kuhlmann as his mother continued singing the beautiful role on TV every Christmas for many years.

Amahl also pioneered the spectacular—a big one-time special show, usually musical, that broke up the monotony of rigid daily scheduling and generated great excitement. The work "spectacular" became current in 1954, thanks to two young men at NBC. Sylvester L. ("Pat") Weaver, a vice president, and newly appointed president Robert Sarnoff (son of David Sarnoff) teamed up to promote the introduction of color television with this idea. They were influenced by the enormous success of one of the greatest performances ever seen on any stage, via any medium—Mary Martin

The first "spectacular" to be given that name, along with an enormous publicity buildup, was Satins and Spurs, *a musical Western starring Betty Hutton, who was at the height of her fame in 1954.*

Mary Martin leaps through the air (on wires) as the flying hero of Peter Pan, *by James M. Barrie, the most successful TV spectacular ever produced. First televised on March 7, 1955, it was viewed by an estimated 5 million enthusiasts and has been restaged a number of times since.*

Following the success of Peter Pan, *other fairy tales were fashioned into colorful spectaculars. Here is Cyril Ritchard in a scene from* Aladdin *in 1957.*

and Ethel Merman on the *Ford 50th Anniversary Show,* June 15, 1953.

Produced by Leland Hayward and telecast by both CBS and NBC, the lavish two-hour program was rich in talent (and short on automobile commercials). Marian Anderson, Howard Lindsay and Dorothy Stickney of *Life With Father,* Edward R. Murrow, Amos 'n' Andy, and others played a part, but the show-stopper came when Martin and Merman, seated on stools on a bare stage, sang a medley in duet. Excitement mounted as each of the women in her own electric style kept topping herself as if trying to sing the other off the stage. One of your authors was in the studio audience; he knew it was a great show, but only the viewer at home, undistracted by studio technical clutter, fully realized how great. By that one performance television grew to maturity on its own merits as a distinctive entertainment form.

However, Pat Weaver's first spectacular in 1954, preceded by elaborate ballyhoo, warned the industry that no amount of publicity could take the place of quality. It featured the TV debut of Betty Hutton in a 90-minute Western musical comedy, *Satins and Spurs.* So disastrous was the reaction that Miss Hutton threatened for awhile to retire from show business. It remained for Mary Martin, again, to score the highwater mark for all spectaculars on March 7, 1955, in Jerome Robbins' production of *Peter Pan.* In two performances the deathless fairy tale captured the largest television audience in history. Like *Amahl* it became a tradition, repeated every second or third year, always greeted with the joy that is the best reward of superior entertainment.

Some top performers, wary of overexposure via television, made the one-shot show their special business. Mary Martin was one, also Maurice Chevalier and Victor Borge, who made their annual appearances beginning in 1956, and Fred Astaire whose hour-long dancing and song show was the biggest TV event in 1958. *An Evening With Fred Astaire,* repeated with new material in succeeding years, stood out for quality amidst daily TV fare which already—even in this Golden Age—showed signs of becoming for the most part routine and witless.

Another major breakthrough came in 1956 when the film, *The Wizard of Oz,* starring Judy Garland and Ray Bolger, was telecast. CBS had purchased the TV rights from MGM. The showing was an immense success, to be repeated every year during the

Actress Julie Andrews (left, in a scene with Edie Adams) played Cinderella *in a 90-minute musical spectacular by Rodgers and Hammerstein. This live show of 1957 was staged again with a different cast for taping in 1965.*

A special one-hour broadcast of The Greatest Show on Earth, *the circus,* in 1955 featured the world-famous clown, Emmett Kelly.

Louis Armstrong, the great jazz trumpeter, in a 1956 television performance. A crumpled handkerchief for mopping his brow was a trademark.

After his initial trial with Arthur Godfrey, Pat Boone went on his own in 1957 as one of the more popular crooners. He does a routine with the telephone on a Thanksgiving Day special in 1962 with Elaine Dunn (left), Patti Page, and grinning Phil Harris.

The "Emmy" award, equivalent to the "Oscar" of the film industry, was passed out to members of the television industry each year in various categories. Art Carney and Nanette Fabray won in 1957 for supporting players.

Art Linkletter exhibited the talent that made him a TV fixture in House Party *in 1952. He interviews a trio of youngsters in this sketch—a specialty in which he is especially adept.*

Christmas season. As a result, however, the price of TV rights to hit movies immediately soared to a prohibitive level, keeping most of them off the home screen to this day.

Topping even *Peter Pan* in size of audience for a single performance was the opening show of *Ford Star Jubilee,* starring Judy Garland in 90 minutes of song, dancing, and small talk with David Wayne. Miss Garland was to repeat this success in the Sixties, but when she attempted a weekly program of her own, the audiences somehow vanished. Television thus demonstrated one of its peculiarities; really great entertainment (as opposed to just good, pretty good, or adequate) could be dispensed via cathode ray only in small doses.

The talkers

Having routed radio in the prime listening hours of the afternoon and evening, the television networks found themselves squeezed for saleable time. They therefore sought to expand in two directions, early morning and late at night. The pioneer late-night variety show was not, as modern listeners might assume, Steve Allen's or Jack Paar's or Johnny Carson's. It was *Broadway Open House,* which began locally on NBC, New York, in 1950 with Morey Amsterdam and later Jerry Lester as master of ceremonies. The idea was for performers to drop in between engagements for small talk or to do impromptu guest shots for the TV audience. Their spontaneous, off-the-cuff material, plus the mad humor of Lester and Dagmar, a statuesque blonde who read bad poetry, gave

The deft skill of Bill and Cora Baird skyrocketed their intricately staged puppets to television popularity in the early Fifties. Besides children's shows, the Baird Marionettes appeared on The Morning Show *with Walter Cronkite and in special productions such as a TV version of* Peter and the Wolf *written for Art Carney.*

Mutual's Merry Mailman *featured Ray Heatherton and became one of the country's* *most popular children's TV programs in the Fifties.*

the listener the feeling he was at a late-night party with some very funny people. The format has persisted to this day. In 1954, it spread from Broadway to the national scene when Steve Allen's daytime show became the *Tonight* show and a network feature. Three years later Jack Paar took over as *Tonight's* host. His feuds and opinions, his hilarious patter with such wits as Alexander King, Hermione Gingold, Dody Goodman, or Zsa Zsa Gabor transformed the mild-appearing Paar into a celebrity with a devoted personal following.

Paar exploited the techniques of monologues, interviews, and situation comedy, surprise endings and clever puns with an easygoing ad lib style that on occasion could be charged with emotion. One night, anioyed by network censorship of a slightly blue joke,

Another popular Walt Disney show on ABC was The Mickey Mouse Club. *The song-leader, Jimmie Dodd, is dressed in the Davy Crockett costume made famous by Fess Parker on* Disneyland.

One of the biggest stars of Disneyland *was the rasp-voiced cartoon character, Donald Duck.*

he walked off the stage in full view of the audience and departed for Hong Kong. He also carried on feuds with columnists Walter Winchell and Dorothy Kilgallen as well as platonic love affairs with people he admired.

Paar started his career as an announcer for the Cleveland Symphony Orchestra, and later became a disk jockey in Buffalo. His comedy capabilities emerged when he entered the Army in 1942 and was assigned to a Special Services troop that entertained the GI's in the Solomon Islands. After the war, he was signed for a summer show on radio, then moved into television via a quiz show.

Another outstanding performer of this breed was Ernie Kovacs, whose wild comic inventiveness was first displayed in a Philadelphia show in 1951. Moving up to the big time a few years later, Kovacs combined a casual, deadpan manner with visual gadgetry unmatched since Charlie Chaplin. He was the first to make full use of television's technical resources for hilarious on-camera effects. When a fatal automobile accident cut short his brilliant career in 1962, many thought that the new medium had lost its first authentic creative genius.

Fred Astaire (here with Barrie Chase) brought his dancing grace to television in two well-received spectaculars in 1958 and 1960.

Victor Borge was one of a number of top performers who confined their TV appearances to a "special" once or twice a year. His unique Comedy In Music *largely one-man show invariably convulsed both audiences and reviewers.*

Helene Stanley and Jack Oakie portrayed a couple of Kansas City burlesque troupers in a musical version of the successful Broadway play, "Burlesque," on the Shower of Stars *series.*

Here, Jack interviews the then Senator John F. Kennedy of Massachusetts.

Before Johnny Carson became a midnight celebrity by taking over the Tonight show from Jack Paar, he already had an enormous amount of television experience as host of both daytime and evening quiz and variety programs. In this 1955 scene from The Johnny Carson Show he introduced the children of show business stars: Mickey Jr. and Timothy Rooney, sons of Mickey Rooney; Richard Skelton, son of Red Skelton; Melinda Marx, daughter of Groucho Marx; and Valentina Skelton, Red's daughter.

At the early morning end of the listening spectrum, another engaging young man, David Garroway, made his mark in 1952 with the *Today* show. He had come from Chicago, where his variety program, *Garroway At Large,* introduced an unhurried, low-key manner that came to be known as the "Chicago school" of conversational TV. Pat Weaver of NBC considered this tone just right for early morning audiences girding themselves to face the day. After a shaky start, Garroway and *Today* developed into a huge commercial success, quickly emulated by other networks. Now hosted by Hugh Downs, formerly Jack Paar's sidekick on the *Tonight* show, this morning melange of news, weather, guest appearances, filmed features, and gentle humor continues to be an American habit and one of TV's biggest money-makers.

Live drama

The appellation "Golden Age" for the Fifties is generally applied in memory of television's initial creative surge into live drama. The medium was fortunate, or perhaps predestined, to enlist a cluster of young talents on their way up. They were not the established Broadway playwrights and Hollywood scenarists, not tired "name" stars of the stage and screen, but brilliant unknowns whose reputations were still to be made. Besides the novelty of television itself, the regularly presented "playhouses" and "showcases" begun in the Forties flourished on the novelty of young ideas, original concepts, fresh points of view which the older media rarely exhibited.

They were exciting years on TV for the stagestruck both behind the scenes and in the audiences. Every night was opening night; one never knew when a flick of the knob would spark the birth of great theatrical literature. But, on the other hand, one never knew when a flick of the knob would lead to an hour of wasted time. This factor—the high percentage of flops, about the same as on Broadway itself—plus the high cost and technical difficulties of staging a new play every week, led to the demise of live TV drama toward the end of the decade. It was replaced by filmed shows made in Hollywood.

Soon the very idea of anthology programming faded out in favor of the series, such as *Gunsmoke* or *Wagon Train,* featuring the same characters every week.

The Today *show was a milestone in the growth years of TV and maintains its wide popularity today. Its original appeal to an early morning audience was the personality of Dave Garroway and the low-keyed tone he set. He is shown here (center) with News editor Frank Blair, Sports editor Jack Lescoulie, and the celebrated chimpanzee, J. Fred Muggs, on their second anniversary in 1953.*

Will Rogers, Jr., with a great deal of the charm and homey philosophy of his late father, conducted a successful morning show in CBS.

The Best of Broadway *presented lavish productions of drama specials, a new concept in 1954. CBS assembled this "dream" cast for "The Man Who Came to Dinner": (left to right) Buster Keaton, Merle Oberon, Joan Bennett, Bert Lahr, Monte Woolley (foreground), and Zasu Pitts.*

Staging a live television show in the Fifties often was as elaborate, complicated, and costly as those on Broadway itself.

In its golden years, however, television drama charted a course unequalled for originality and verve since the Elizabethan theatre that produced William Shakespeare. Except for news coverage, live drama fulfilled better than any other type of program the real purpose behind the invention of television. From the beginning, the uniqueness of the medium lay in its ability to present events that were happening at the very moment they were happening. This meant a tightly-structured play directed not at the millions of people "out there," but at the two or three persons sitting in one living room. The keyed-up acting created the effect of someone coming into your home to tell you a true story. Even fluffs and boners by the actors added to the impact. Such intimacy was impossible in any other medium; its loss in the more slickly contrived, mass-oriented Hollywood product is unquestionably to be regretted.

While the bad TV plays are forgotten, the great ones were superb. Sometimes they were fine productions of the classics, as when Helen Hayes in *Victoria Regina* inaugurated the *Robert Montgomery Presents* series in 1950. More often they were originals. *Marty,* by Paddy Chayefsky, which appeared on *Television Playhouse* one memorable night in 1953, became a classic with the next morning's reviews. Rod Steiger played the forlorn Bronx butcher and Nancy Marchand his homely girl; Delbert Mann directed. When *Marty* became a movie, Mann again directed with no loss of mood or taste, indeed with a gain in authentic on-location sequences. With *Marty,* the television tail began to wag the motion picture dog.

Other TV plays of the Fifties that also became part of the modern repertoire included *A Man Is Ten Feet Tall* (1955) by Robert Alan Aurthur, with Sidney Poitier in the cast; *Twelve Angry Men* (1954) by Reginald Rose; *Patterns* (1955) by Rod Serling; *A Profile in Courage* (1956), based on the book by the 36-year-old Senator John F. Kennedy; *A Night to Remember* (1956) on the sinking of the Titanic, with over 100 actors on 30 sets in a production triumph for director George Roy Hill; *Little Moon of Alban* (1958) by James Costigan, with Julie Harris in the cast; *Requiem for a Heavyweight* (1956) by Rod Serling, with Jack Palance, Keenan Wynn, his father Ed Wynn, and Kim Hunter; and *The Days of Wine and Roses* (1958) by J. P. Miller.

Increasingly, television became a source of talent for the movies and legitimate theatre. The emergence of the medium from the

Behind the scenes live television drama entailed as much thought and stress as every first night on Broadway. Alex Segal, director of many shows for U.S. Steel Hour, Producers Showcase, and Theater Guild productions is shown discussing the play "P.O.W." with members of the cast (Brian Keith at right).

One reason why live television drama had its problems was the studio heat. While Wally Cox and Betsy Palmer had to wear winter clothes under the lights for their roles in "The Meanest Man" on United States Steel Hour, cameraman George King found relief in more appropriate off-camera attire.

Art Carney and "friend" were the
principals in the comedy "Harvey"
on Du Pont Show of the Month.

Richard Kiley, Everett Sloane and
Ed Begley starred in Rod Serling's
memorable drama of big business,
"Patterns."

Playhouse 90 *presented Jack Palance and Kim Hunter in "Requiem for a Heavy-weight," another of Rod Serling's distinguished dramas. Ed and Keenan Wynn also starred.*

status of an experimental stage—the off-Broadway of mass entertainment—was foreshadowed by two events. One was a settlement of the TV-Hollywood feud. After a costly advertising campaign using the slogan, "Movies Are Better Than Ever," the motion picture industry threw in the sponge. It decided that if it couldn't fight TV, it would "join 'em." In 1955, most of the major studios began to produce films specifically for television. Companies such as Warner Brothers, 20th Century Fox, Columbia, Republic, and MGM set up subsidiary organizations to turn out half-hour and hour-long dramas for the home tube. In addition, as television prospered, the networks became financially capable of meeting the price for older films that had been produced for the movies years before.

From the viewers' point of view, the acquisition of Hollywood resources may or may not have been a gain. The film-makers' idea

"The Day Lincoln Was Shot" was a 90-minute Jubilee *dramatization of Jim Bishop's best-selling book, with Raymond Massey as Lincoln and Lillian Gish as Mrs. Lincoln. The opening scene shows the President's family at breakfast; the drama ended with the final pressing of two silver coins on the dead man's eyelids. Jack Lemmon played John Wilkes Booth and Charles Laughton was narrator of this distinguished special.*

Julie Harris and Christopher Plummer in a scene from James Costigan's play, "Little Moon of Alban" for Hallmark Hall of Fame. The play was repeated some years later with Dirk Bogarde (right) replacing Plummer.

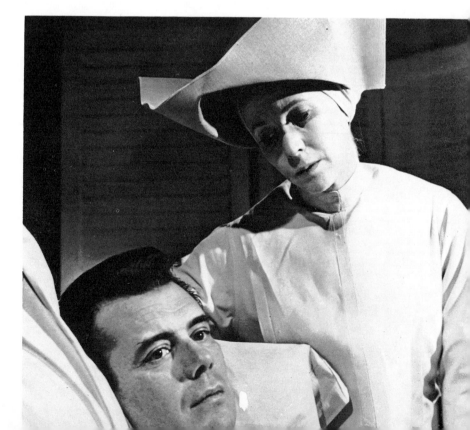

of original dramatic fare for TV was generally vapid, while the old films squeezed newer material off the air. Beginning with *Studio One* in 1958, one dramatic show after the other either slipped out to the West Coast, or closed shop with sad, nostalgic notices that they were happy to have served in the past and hoped to return in the future. They never did.

The second event in the emergence of TV was the introduction of video tape in 1957. This was one of few inventions ever created on command, the command coming from Bing Crosby and other TV entertainers who lived in California. When popular variety shows were telecast live, it was necessary for Crosby, Bob Hope, and company to perform twice in order to catch prime listening time in all parts of the country. (For example, at 7 P.M. Eastern Standard Time, and repeat three hours later at 7 P.M. Pacific Time.) Audio tape had already solved the time difference problem for sound broadcasting. Crosby conveniently had invested in a research organization which he promptly charged with finding a way to record sight as well as sound on tape.

Developed simultaneously by Bing Crosby Enterprises, Ampex,

Noel Coward co-starred with Edna Best in the hit British play, "This Happy Breed," on Ford Star Jubilee *in 1956.*

Piper Laurie and Cliff Robertson played the alcoholics in J. P. Miller's "The Days of Wine and Roses" on Playhouse 90.

Orson Welles and Betty Grable in "The Twentieth Century," another Jubilee *presentation of a famous Broadway play.*

and RCA, video tape did revolutionize TV programming. Unlike the kinescope (TV transferred to film), taping was instantaneous, relatively inexpensive, and almost perfect in fidelity. It permitted the play-back of material without processing, as well as editing out errors or improving upon a rehearsal. Because it was completely electronic—no films, records, prints, chemicals, etc., to bother with —taping· gave the medium enormous flexibility. Used properly, as in instantly capturing and repeating a big moment of a news or sports event, tape was undeniably a boon. Used without conscience, alas, it also contributed to eliminating the last elements of spontaneity—and thereby believability—from much television programming, both dramatic and reportorial.

Lucy and company

One of the reasons for filming and taping TV programs was money—savings in cost plus the returns from so-called syndication, or repeat performances. A live show lived only for its hour, and was paid only for its hour or so on the air, but a filmed show could receive residual payments for years (e.g., *I Love Lucy*) and from all over the world (*Perry Mason*). Even commercials became highly

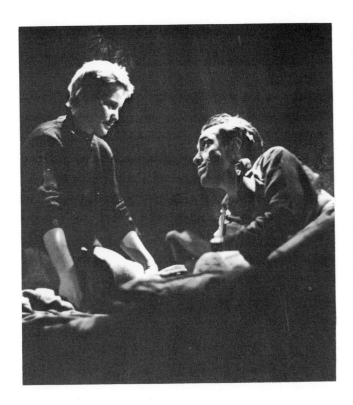

One of Playhouse 90's *finest achievements was the presentation of Ernest Hemingway's "For Whom the Bell Tolls" in two consecutive ninety-minute shows in 1959. Maria Schell and Jason Robards, Jr. starred.*

A scene from the adaptation of Wilder's "The Bridge of San Luis Rey," starring Hume Cronyn, Viveca Linfors, Eva LeGallienne, Rita Gam and Judith Anderson. Theodore Bikel also starred.

A new phenomenon was born with Westinghouse's sponsorship of Studio One—*the immergence of the commercial star. Betty Furness, later to be head of Consumer Affairs for the Johnson Administration, delivering her famous line, "You can be sure if it's Westinghouse" became a nationwide celebrity.*

Ronald Reagan was first the star and later the host on the General Electric Theater, *a weekly drama series which opened in 1953. He is shown here with Carol Lynley and Agnes Moorehead.*

profitable for actors of the caliber of Edward G. Robinson or Ed Wynn; every time a taped commercial was shown, which might be 100 times in a week, another "residual" lined the actor's pocket.

Another reason was television's rediscovery of the serial story. Situation comedies became the comic strips of the new medium, built around one or two characters appearing each week in a different story line. They could be ground out by the yard, filmed or taped or both, and placed with TV stations for runs and reruns whenever convenient. Most of them (like most comic strips) were trash, but a few (like a few comic strips) revealed the unmistakable class of the true craftsman.

The greatest no doubt was *I Love Lucy*, starring film comedienne Lucille Ball and her then husband Desi Arnaz. Beginning in 1951, the series achieved heights of popularity unmatched even by Milton Berle in the early days or by any later comedy show on American television. Miss Ball played a young wife with a penchant for farcical misunderstandings, aided and abetted by her "straight man" husband, a Cuban bandleader, and their neighbors, played by William Frawley and Vivian Vance. The original

"Television City" constructed by CBS in Hollywood in 1952 marked the end of an era for television—the big switch from live dramatic shows to the filmed product. This 35-acre complex was in effect a complete motion picture studio designed especially for the electronic medium. It put TV production for the first time on an efficient and economical assembly-line basis.

As The World Turns *has been the all-time champion among the "soap operas" since it went on the air in 1956. In one of its less heart-rending episodes Helen Wagner (center), Don McLaughlin and other members of the cast discuss a family happening.*

series on film or tape ran and reran throughout the world, and built Miss Ball's producing company, Desilu, into a Hollywood giant of the new era.

Filmed series of the same type included *Ozzie and Harriet* (Nelson), *Father Knows Best* with Robert Young, *Make Room for Daddy* with Danny Thomas, *Mr. Peepers* with Wally Cox, *Our Miss Brooks* with Eve Arden, *Private Secretary* with Ann Sothern, *Topper,* and literally scores of others that came and went with the fickle tides of popularity. The contrived situations and canned laughter (since there was no studio audience) may not have con-

Portia Faces Life was a popular daytime serial starring Fran Carlon, Carl Swenson, Charles Taylor, and Ginger McManus. Called "soap operas" because often sponsored by laundry products, these serials had a dedicated following among legions of housewives.

Love of Life, *another soap opera, began in the early fifties. Richard Coogan and Peggy McCay are the performers.*

110

Sheree North and Jack Benny were guests on the premiere of The Bing Crosby Show.

The Edge of Night *has been popular since its appearance in 1956. Here the original principals, John Larkin and Teal Ames, come to grips with a marital problem.*

A demonstration of Ampex recording (video) tape at a CBS studio in 1955 promised a revolution in television broadcasting that actually took place. The electronic tape recorded instantaneous sight and sound and permitted immediate playback without processing. It also produced a more faithful reproduction than film.

tributed much to American literature, but did have an unexpected cultural influence. They uniformly depicted American middle-class family life, which created a social norm. Radio shows had done likewise, but the listener had to imagine the sets. He could furnish them with his own ideas of what was suitable. On TV he *saw* the middle-class homes, the cars, the appliances, and if he did not own the same, he coveted them. The marches of the poor a decade later could be directly traced to this reaction. So could the "hippie" rebellion of the affluent young, who saw their middle-class treasures depicted as commonplace and therefore empty.

NBC photo of the same period shows how video tape feeds through a series of electronic "heads" to record magnetic patterns that will duplicate both images and sounds.

Vivian Vance and William Frawley (flanking Miss Ball) played the Ricardo neighbors, Fred and Ethel Mertz. Tennessee Ernie Ford (center) was a guest star in this 1951 show.

I Love Lucy, *starring Desi Arnaz and Lucille Ball began in 1951 and now rates as a classic of television technique. It combined clever writing and inventive gags with superb clowning by Miss Ball, a hint of drama and the illusion of real life going on from week to week. The characters of Ricky and Lucy Ricardo were actually as well as fictionally husband and wife (they were divorced some years later), and most of the situations were built around conjugal misunderstandings such as an overheard telephone conversation.*

In this episode, Ricky is acquiring an unexpected veneer from the business end of a paint sprayer, solemnly observed by Richard Deacon (center).

Raymond Burr (here with Ruta Lee) breathed life into the Perry Mason show as a criminal lawyer who almost always liberated his client from the clutches of the district attorney. The show began in 1957 and ran for nine years.

George Burns (right) and the late Gracie Allen had their own immensely popular show in the Fifties. This episode involved a gym instructor played by Steve Reeves, later the hero of "Hercules" and other muscular film epics.

Ozzie and Harriet *was one of the earliest family comedy shows making its debut in 1952. Ozzie and Harriet, together with their two sons, Ricky and David, played the same roles as they did in real life.*

Cops and cowboys

In addition to situation comedy, television drama converted itself into serious (or at least non-funny) action serials. Unlike the earlier *Hopalong Cassidy* genre, these were aimed at adult audiences. *Wyatt Earp* pioneered on ABC in 1955, followed almost at once by *Gunsmoke* on CBS. The latter was the first Western to successfully challenge a major comedian, George Gobel, whose Saturday night show it displaced in the ratings. Others were *Have Gun, Will Travel* and *Wagon Train*. *Bonanza* which, beginning in 1959, grew into the top-rated show on Sunday nights and stayed there year after year. It signaled a departure; the guns of the heroes and villains barked, all right, but not continuously. *Bonanza's* story lines were akin to soap opera, about the troubles of people, with tugs at the heart along with the thudding of hooves.

Life With Father, the long-running Broadway play, was adapted for television in 1953 with Leon Ames as Clarence Day Sr. and Lurene Tuttle as his wife Vinnie. It became a popular family comedy series.

Imogene Coca, who became a star with Sid Caesar's troupe on The Show of Shows, *had her own comedy show in 1954. She is shown doing a farcical scene with Hiram Sherman.*

Originally entitled You'll Never Get Rich, *the* Sergeant Bilko Show *rocketed Phil Silvers to overnight success in 1955. Silvers played the role of Ernie Bilko, the Army sergeant with fantastic avarice, who led his platoon of soldiers through hilarious antics. Writer Nat Hiken created the series.*

In 1956, Phil Silvers won three Emmy Awards for his performances as Sergeant Bilko.

In The Bob Cummings Show, *the star played a photographer who always seemed to be surrounded by beautiful girls. When the comedian played dramatic parts, he was known as Robert Cummings.*

Danny Thomas became a television star in the program, Make Room For Daddy, *a situation comedy later renamed* The Danny Thomas Show. *Thomas, who had been a night club entertainer for more than ten years, played the role with unusual warmth and sympathy, because it paralleled his own life. He was born in 1914 and got most of his theatrical experience at a local radio station and then in vaudeville. His TV success beginnings in 1953 led to his creating a producing organization that controlled several shows.*

A similar trend appeared in crime serials, beginning with the immensely popular *Dragnet*, featuring Jack Webb, in 1952. *The Untouchables*, a Desilu production of 1958, had Walter Winchell narrating the FBI war with the Capone gang as if the episodes were fact, not fiction. Such shows as 77 *Sunset Strip, I Spy* with Raymond Massey, *I Led Three Lives*, and *Naked City* employed authentic big city backgrounds, stories derived from actual police cases, and low-keyed, laconic delivery of the actors' lines to assume the appearance of a documentary. More and more, writers for television found that reality—or a reasonable semblance thereof—was the medium's strongest appeal. *Victory At Sea*, filmed history of the Navy's role in World War II, with music by Richard Rodgers, began its run on NBC in 1952 and outdid all of its quasi-fictional rivals in popularity and long life.

Culture on TV

Early in the Fifties, the cultural implication of the national television habit began to worry thoughtful people. It was not so much that most TV programming, from their point of view, was bad art. All previous forms of mass entertainment, aimed at a level of popular taste well below the college graduate's, had been equally bad art. Most movies were grade B or worse, most novels were pot-boilers, comic books were atrocious, best-selling "pop" records were hardly Beethoven. Beginning way back in Shakesperian times

The versatile Dick Powell tried his hand at Western parts in his series, Zane Grey Theater.

The TV adult Western began as the ostensibly true biography of Wyatt Earp. This developed into an ABC fictional series in 1955, and continued running for many years. Hugh O'Brian (left) played the lawman.

121

CBS found the richest pay dirt in Westerns with Gunsmoke in 1955, which muscled its way to No. 1 ratings on Saturday nights and stayed there for more than ten years. The chief characters were Marshal Matt Dillon (James Arness) comforting Miss Kitty (Amanda Blake) with the aid of drawling, limping Deputy Chester Goode (Dennis Weaver).

Willard Parker in Tales of the Texas Rangers.

Robert Horton and Ward Bond were the original principals in the popular Western, Wagon Train.

Clint Walker was the rugged hero of Cheyenne.

Richard Boone (left) was the suave gun-for-hire in the Western series, Have Gun, Will Travel.

James Garner starred in the Western spoof, Maverick. Jack Kelly (right) appeared some years later as his brother Bart.

Actor-director Jack Webb showed the grimy side of police operations when he launched the realistic Dragnet *in 1952. Here he is rehearsing a nurse's aide from Los Angeles, Mrs. Mary Bigler, a participant in an actual case of robbery-kidnapping, who portrayed herself on the program in 1958.*

Alfred Hitchcock shown coaching Vincent Price, who played a famous detective in the mystery drama, "The Perfect Crime," on Alfred Hitchcock Presents in 1957.

Steve Allen, best known as a comic m.c. on Tonight *and other conversational shows, also composed music and wrote plays. This 1953 photo shows him in a role of his own authorship on the* Danger *series, a story about a derelict piano player and a Eurasian beauty, played by his wife Jayne Meadows in a dark wig.*

Dr. Baxter and actor Eddie Albert in a scene from "Our Mr. Sun" in the Bell Telephone science series.

most stage plays ever written have been poor, including some of Shakespeare's. The new problem raised by TV was the *saturation* of the public's leisure time with the inferior, the cynically commercial, the meretricious, the sensational. Whereas people might have seen a movie a week, attended a play a month, read one novel a year—they watched TV an average of *five hours every day.* And since the electronic message now penetrated the sanctuary of the home, the restraints of discipline and discrimination among viewers broke down. Children could be guarded against exposure to horror movies or salacious novels, but short of threatening them with a knotted club, they could not be prevented from watching violence on TV. Meanwhile the older, better educated, more experienced and discriminating members of the audience, quickly satiated by the race for ratings or repelled by the mediocrity, turned away from the tube altogether. (Spectaculars, news coverage, and sports were among TV's efforts to win them back.)

The live dramas, mentioned earlier in this book, left a void as they disappeared, one by one, victims of the advertiser's implacable search for more sales return per TV dollar. In 1952 the Ford Foundation attempted to reverse the trend by heavily subsidizing a frankly cultural program, *Omnibus.* Telecast on CBS for 90 minutes each week, with the urbane Alistair Cooke as host, *Omnibus* ventured into earnest drama (*King Lear, Oedipus Rex, Mr. Lincoln* and a serial by James Agee, among others), into symphonic music with Leonard Bernstein, into sophisticated comedy with Mike Nichols and Elaine May, into ballet, into education in all the fine arts. *Omnibus* tried hard, as did *The Seven Lively Arts* (1957), David Susskind's *Du Pont Show of the Month, Ford Startime,* and others of similar good intentions, but their eventual demise was written in red ink. One problem, of course, was the inevitable spottiness of the material offered. Television audiences, once disappointed, tend to turn the knob (it's so easy to do) and rarely give a failure another chance. The good intentions did not die, however, but found a new outlet in the rise of a separate educational television network in the Sixties.

Politics and sports

The 1952 presidential election marked the takeover by TV of the role of prime mover in American politics. First, the political

Dr. Frank Baxter in the early Fifties brought Shakespeare to television audiences with a brilliant analysis of the Bard's plays and sonnets. The enthusiastic response established the appeal of scholarly material; Baxter subsequently handled a science show for Bell Telephone.

Richard Boone acting the leading role on Medic in 1954. Mr. Boone's show was the first medical drama series and was widely acclaimed for its realistic portrayal of hospital problems and practices.

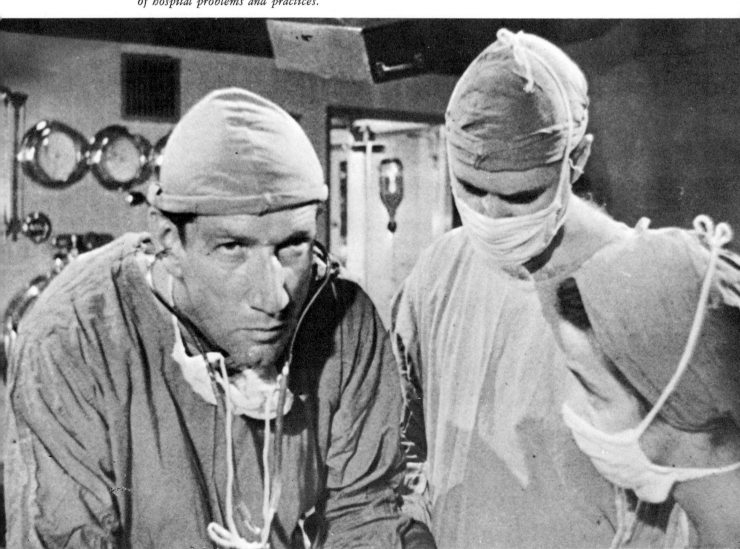

Alistair Cooke, a transplanted Englishman, was the urbane master of ceremonies on NBC's Omnibus. He is shown discussing a program on American trial by jury with Joseph N. Welch, Boston lawyer and hero of the Army-McCarthy hearings.

Omnibus was an outstanding vehicle for high grade dramatic and artistic material, partially sponsored commercially and partially subsidized by a foundation. The scene is the burning of Joan of Arc in a specially written drama for the CBS program. Kim Stanley starred.

conventions, which had been fitfully covered by gallery cameras since 1940, developed into the new medium's biggest quadrennial show. Senator Kefauver shattered a precedent by appearing at the Democratic Convention although himself a candidate. The camera caught him in the gallery with face flushed and teeth gritted as the delegates roundly booed his unconventionality. In Chicago, America received its introduction to the famous grin and upswept arms of President-to-be Eisenhower.

As the campaign got under way, Eisenhower's running-mate, Senator Richard M. Nixon, was accused of accepting $18,000 in expense money from a group of California backers. Some Republican party leaders demanded his withdrawal from the race; instead, Nixon asked for time on television to appeal directly to the American people. In a famous speech (or infamous, depending on the partisan point of view), he asserted he was a poor man, that his wife wore a cloth coat, and that the only personal gift he had

"The Kremlin" was a panorama of Russian history presented on the program Odyssey, *which re-created historical events such as the seizure of power by Nicolai Lenin.*

Bishop Fulton J. Sheen, shown here with Ed Sullivan in 1956, began broadcasting weekly sermons on ABC television on a schedule that competed with Milton Berle's immensely popular program. Berle, called "Uncle Miltie," mischievously referred to the Bishop as "Uncle Fultie." Sheen won great popularity himself, and religious programming has continued to be a televison staple.

Lamp Unto My Feet *presented dramatizations of religious themes. This scene shows Siobhan McKenna reading verses for a 1956 Sunday morning program.*

In 1956 television election coverage expanded in a dozen different directions to bring both the news and its interpretation to masses of listeners. The Congressional Close-Up program provided interesting sidelights from Representatives in Congress.

Nikita Khrushchev occasionally cracked the ice of the cold war a little by giving his views of the world situation, as in this scene from a CBS program of 1957, Face the Nation.

accepted was a little dog named Checkers for his young daughters. In an early demonstration of television's awesome power to influence voters, Nixon remained on the GOP ticket and was elected Vice President.

During the next eight years the Eisenhower administration was to use television as FDR used radio. Presidential press conferences were televised; no longer would national leaders be mere voices on radio or shadows caught briefly in photographs. Television gave them body and personality. It also gave them art, which could be used to deflect the medium's X-ray eye from seeing too much.

Programs such as *Meet the Press,* begun in 1947, *Face the Nation, Mike Wallace Interviews, CBS Reports* with Walter Cronkite, *The Huntley-Brinkley Report,* and Murrow's *Person to Person* put political (and other) celebrities on public view every week as they answered searching questions from skilled reporters. Because Sunday afternoon was "politics time" on TV, politicians began making a habit of using these shows for major announcements, thus assuring front-page coverage in the Monday papers.

The 1956 Republican Convention created the team of Chet Huntley, a veteran TV newsman, and wryly humorous David Brinkley. Their knowledgeable but entertaining colloquies brought the political shenanigans on the floor into meaningful focus. The 1956 Democratic Convention is especially remembered for a vignette of Jacqueline Kennedy (who was pregnant at the time) seated in the gallery surrounded by friends while her husband made his bid for the vice-presidential nomination. At the last moment the delegates turned to Kefauver. Suddenly the camera showed Mrs. Kennedy seated all alone, smiling wanly but bravely, a forlorn picture of disappointment.

On January 20, 1953, President Eisenhower's inauguration was the first to be seen from coast to coast. That year, too, television covered the coronation of Queen Elizabeth, while CBS devoted more than 55 hours to live United Nations sessions in Manhattan. And in December, the FCC finally approved color standards for compatible telecasting, embarking the industry on a new phase that eventually would encompass real life programs as well as entertainment.

Among the first live telecasts in color were the Cotton Bowl and Rose Bowl football games of January 1, 1954. The total of TV sets in American homes rose to over 34 million. The effect of such saturation on the American way of life, a powerful force not yet fully understood, found its first documentation in the world of sports. Stated briefly, TV transformed the athletic American male from a participant into a spectator, killed off all but the top professional athletic organizations, and destroyed the local breeding grounds of talent. As vaudeville had been ruined by network variety shows, so were baseball's minor leagues and boxing's neighborhood clubs.

Television brought viewers the greatest fighters of the day, Rocky Marciano, Joe Wolcott, Ray Robinson, Archie Moore, Kid Gavilan, every Wednesday, Friday, and in some places Saturday as well. Tube-watchers witnessed the swan song of Joe Louis and the rise of a new breed—but it was too good to last. As the battle-scarred veterans of the small club circuit faded from the scene, their replacements became increasingly amateurish and cautious, the contests more and more soporific. So boxing became a casualty of saturation. Soon a heavyweight championship would be shown

Mike Wallace initiated a new method of television reporting with his Nightbeat *program on Dumont's New York station WABD. He did depth interviewing and probed into the life story of each guest, as with Gloria Swanson in this 1957 photo. The popularity of this local show projected Wallace into national prominence as a newscaster.*

Moving to the ABC network, Wallace interviewed people all over the world. To present Kirk Douglas, he flew to Munich where the film star was making a picture. The filmed interview was flown back to the U.S.A. for televising.

"The name of the program is Person to Person." These words opened this famous show every week starting in 1953. Edward R. Murrow, with the magic of electronics, "visited" the homes of prominent people throughout the country and interviewed them from a CBS studio. His dynamic personality and intelligent questioning helped to place the program among the 20 most popular in the country for several years.

Chet Huntley and David Brinkley proved to be an overwhelming success when they teamed to present the 1956 political conventions for NBC. Their straightforwardness and subtle wit delighted viewers and has made them the most acclaimed team in newscasting ever since.

In 1956 computers joined the election reporting staff; they appraised the constantly changing returns and, after a few false starts, became accurate in predicting final results many hours before the actual polls had closed. This was UNIVAC, with newsman Douglas Edwards and a technician, Richard De Loach.

The 1956 version of communication equipment for the convention floor, carried by Douglas Edwards. It enabled newsmen to interview delegates while being picked up by cameras in press-radio gallery.

Armed with computers and modern methods of sampling the voting population, pollsters increased the range, accuracy, and authority of their straw votes until they came to exercise great influence on political decisions. Here Elmo Roper (center) discusses the polling art with Harold Stassen and Senator Styles Bridges of New Hampshire on a CBS news program.

only on closed circuit TV in theatres, with a ringside audience often not much larger than the working press.

Major league baseball, on the other hand, appeared to benefit from television exposure. The leagues expanded to the West Coast, and gate receipts continued high. There were signs, however, of deterioration both in the quality of play and in the loyalty of the spectators, a majority of whom now appeared to be less than 14 years old and lured by promotions rather than by interest in the game. Professional football became *the* national pastime because football, despite TV, retained its breeding ground of talent on the college gridirons. When teams were successful, tickets were scarce, and since local telecasts were often blanked out, enthusiasts would motor 75 miles outside the local area to catch the game on TV in a motel or tavern.

The denouement

The year 1956 may be considered a highwater mark in the rise of television. Two out of three American families now owned at least one set, and sat, eyes glued to· the screens, by day and by night. The habit of reading declined. Most affected were magazines of general interest and "trade" (non-specialized) hardcover books. Newspapers began to change in character, becoming more interpretive than reportorial. Those that could not successfully effect the transition were forced out of business. Sometimes it seemed that people had stopped talking to one another, too. They neither read the news nor discussed it; they left all that to the one-way communication of the television tube.

By this time many children attending high school could not remember what life was like without TV. The medium had grown to a network of 78,000 channel miles, making possible intercity connection of 440 stations in 300 cities. Audiences at times were prodigious. In August 1956, during the political conventions, it was possible for 90 per cent of all Americans to watch the proceedings "live," and an estimated seven out of ten families did so. But a highwater mark implies an ebbing of the tide to follow, and the downturn for TV came for a reason that would be laughable if the consequences were not so serious.

The era of the big-money quiz began in 1955 with *The $64,000 Question.* The fact that it grew out of radio's *The $64*

The 1952 presidential election was the first in which television played a significant role. While the national conventions had been televised as early as 1940, only a small audience in a limited area could watch them. By 1952 the medium had the attention of millions of Americans. In all its pageantry and boredom, solemnity and nonsense, the quadrennial conclaves of Republicans and Democrats became essentially a TV show. Events on the floor were rearranged to capture prime time on camera, windy speeches were cut down in length if not in number, and TV reporters with walkie-talkies swarmed about to be picked out by zoom cameras while they squeezed rumor and fact out of famous men.

Lull before the storm: Eric Sevareid, Edward R. Murrow, Walter Cronkite, and Lowell Thomas awaiting the onrush of election night returns that would soon indicate a landslide victory for Dwight D. Eisenhower.

When Sam Levenson became a summer replacement on Two For The Money *in 1956, he built up one of the highest ratings for a summer show in television history. A master story teller, Levenson had brought a new comedy format to his own program in 1950, and to panel shows and guest spots through the years. He found a smile in almost every situation, especially in the memories of his tenement childhood in New York and his early career as a public school teacher of Spanish.*

Question merely reflected the dizzying heights of television's financial inflation. The show proved so popular that it was quickly followed with even larger prizes for odd information, *The Big Surprise* ($100,000), and *Twenty-One*. Watching the contestants struggle for these awesome hoards became a national fixation; viewers sweated for them in their "isolation booths" and writhed when they missed. Seemingly elaborate precautions were taken to prevent prompting or advance leakage of a correct answer. And that was the trouble.

The producers soon discovered that contestants who were memory wizards but nothing else were dull. A mild Italian cobbler who knew more about opera than Rudolph Bing, a little old lady who outdid Casey Stengel on baseball lore, a horse jockey who could out-talk a museum curator about art . . . these had personality, audience identification with the underdog, sex appeal, they were *fun*. Rumors began to fly that in the name of entertainment, the more colorful contestants were being favored; that is, the shows were rigged. Finally, in 1958, a defeated contestant on a show called *Dotto* blew the whistle. The accusation exploded on the public with a shocking surprise. A district attorney investigated, then a grand jury, finally a congressional committee.

Early glib denials developed into confessions of wholesale cheating; ten persons pleaded guilty to perjury before the grand jury. Careers were ruined. But the real victim was television itself. The American people were devastated by the Quiz Scandal because their faith had been betrayed. Actually there had been nothing illegal about faked quiz answers any more than Houdini's magic tricks were illegal. But that is show-business morality; people wanted to believe in television as the real thing, not as a stage illusion. Neither the people nor the medium would ever again regain their innocence. The image was tarnished for good.

By this time, in Washington, Senators and Congressmen were taking courses in the art of speaking before the television camera. The "actor's smile" replaced the "salesman's handshake" as the politician's chief vote-gathering weapon. Delegates at the big conventions were officially warned not to pick their noses lest the camera eye be upon them. The conventions themselves came to be "rigged" in the sense of being tailored to television timing and audience impatience with windy rhetoric. The once clear dividing line between fact and illusion became somewhat indistinct. In 1958 a credibility gap opened between television and its audience.

This Is Your Life *was brought over from radio by Ralph Edwards. In the show Edwards presented the life stores of interesting personalities, the gimmick being to surprise the subject by bringing his relatives, old friends, childhood teachers, etc., on the show. This scene shows Edwards with comedian Lou Costello and his mother.*

The big-money quiz shows began with Lou Cowan's The $64,000 Question, *and set a new pattern of television entertainment throughout the world. Huge cash prizes, isolation booths, and encyclopedic memories aroused tremendous interest among millions of delighted televisions viewers. In front of the isolation booth, quizzmaster Hal March gives a successful contestant some reference books to read in preparation for next week's more difficult questions and bigger stakes. The consolation prize for losers was a new Cadillac.*

Child prodigy Robert Strom of The Bronx, New York, was a "regular" of the quiz shows and won a small fortune in prizes before the bubble burst with the great rigging scandal of 1958. In this 1957 episode of Giant Step he used a computer to solve a problem posed by his father, Albert Strom (left) and Anthony Stoeckert.

Ralph Story (center) briefs three contestants on The $64,000 Challenge.

Martha Raye reached the top with her own brand of comedy in 1953. She mixes it up in a typical sequence with Rocky Graziano and Jake La Motta, former championship boxers.

Nat King Cole (right), shown here with Frankie Laine, was a sensation on his own show beginning in 1957 but he vanished from the air waves after two years because no advertiser would sponsor him.

The Golden Age was over. The gap has never been completely closed.

No comedian in his right mind before the coming of TV would have dreamed of going to the same house once a week and being the life of the party, yet this is what he tries to do on video. It is a madness, and the toll of comedians is one of TV's greatest tragedies. The country needs its warm and funny men too much to burn them out. The comedians should restrain their appearances to a few performances a year. Failing that, the viewer can only institute his own rationing system.

Top stars such as Milton Berle, Sid Caesar, Red Buttons, Buddy Hackett, Wally Cox, and Martha Raye were either struggling to maintain their programs or had already lost them. Other stars like Jack Benny, Bob Hope, Jerry Lewis, and Jimmy Durante either deliberately limited their exposure in a successful effort to maintain popularity, or like Danny Kaye, warily avoided the voracious tube altogether.

A similar attrition affected other types of TV entertainment. A situation comedy or "action" series had to catch on quick or wind up in the ashcan within weeks. Playing safe, producers would hasten to imitate any show scoring even a modest success. When the adult Western arrived, the number of them multiplied until in 1959 a total of 32—virtually indistinguishable from one another in plot, characters, or appeal—were crowding the prime evening hours. The result was a leveling and sameness among programs that led in logical steps from monotony to boredom to complete rejection by some segments of the viewer population.

Meanwhile in real life a series of extraordinary events was expanding television's audience for news and for dramatic programming derived from the news. In 1956, besides Adlai Stevenson's memorable campaign for the presidency, there was the crisis at Suez and Israel's lightning invasion of the Sinai peninsula of Egypt. Nikita Khrushchev, having denounced the memory of Josef Stalin for his "crimes," crushed a revolt in Hungary with Stalinistic ruthlessness. In October 1957, America's faith in her technological superiority vanished into space with the orbiting of Sputnik I, Russia's (and mankind's) first artificial earth satellite. When the United States duplicated the feat in January 1958 by launching Explorer I at Cape Canaveral, a "race to the Moon" began. Televi-

Sultry singer Eartha Kitt as a guest star on The Big Record, *1957.*

Lawrence Welk (right) brought "champagne music" with soothing orchestration into the American living room.

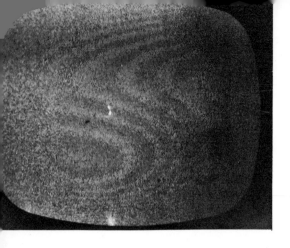

This was the Soviet Sputnik No. 2, carrying the dog Laika, as TV watchers saw it on John Daly's ABC news program in 1957. The historic half-ton orbiting satellite was caught on film by camerman Larry Johnson, who used a six-inch lens from a "moon watch" station atop a St. Louis building.

Another technique in educational TV is demonstrated by Charlotte Robinson, a teacher in the St. Louis public schools, who used blocks to put across a spelling lesson. Station KETC, St. Louis, devoted part of its regular broadcasting time to direct instruction in public school classrooms.

sion brought home to the viewer a new kind of *true* drama no mere fiction-writer could equal.

Television also asserted itself in the making (as well as reporting) of history when, in 1957, President Eisenhower sent troops to Little Rock, Arkansas, to enforce Federal laws for the desegregation of public schools. For the first time the average American was able to envisage the alienation and strivings of the Negro citizen; the beginnings of civil rights militancy and the echo of "black power" in the Sixties may readily be traced to TV coverage of the Little Rock incident and its successors elsewhere.

Across the Florida Straits in Cuba, Fidel Castro seized power in 1959, and based his control of the nation upon marathon telecasts during which he sometimes spoke continuously for six or seven hours. Later in the year Khrshchev visited the United States for the first time and, as it turned out later, the two events were not unrelated. During his visit the Soviet premier appeared on a remarkable TV program which wound up with the interviewer, David Susskind, receiving a lecture on the Marxist "system." Previously Khrushchev had similarly exchanged insults on Soviet television with Vice President Nixon, during the latter's visit to an exhibit of kitchen equipment in Moscow. Oddly enough, these seemingly fierce confrontations marked a turn in the cold war. Penetrating through every mask, the eye of TV exposed the Russians to Americans (and vice versa) as human beings after all, even though a mite peculiar.

Subscription (pay) television

The technical capabilities of TV increased steadily with advances in color reception, zoom lenses, the split screen, and automatic microwave relays for long distance transmission, supplementing the coaxial cable. Small towns were hooked into metropolitan telecasts by means of lofty community antennas (CATV). Since these antenna systems charged a monthly fee per set attached, they raised new questions concerning the ownership of programs thus picked out of the air. (The Supreme Court ruled in the Sixties in favor of CATV.) Meanwhile the programming direction taken by commercial television prompted proposals as early as 1950 that some channels be allotted to non-commercial, subscription TV.

The idea of subscription or toll television was to use certain allotted frequencies for transmission of special programs that for proper reception would require a payment from viewers. This plan would divorce some television schedules from advertising sponsorship. By such means, it was hoped, programs of higher creative or cultural quality could be financed and presented, without being squeezed into a rigid time schedule or chopped up to make room for commercials.

In 1952 the Zenith Radio Corporation petitioned the FCC to authorize pay TV on a regular basis, using a system called Phonevision. A similar petition was received in 1954 for Subscriber-Vision. Three other systems presented in 1957 were called Telemeter, Teleglobe, and Bi-Tran. The FCC authorized a trial period of three years for the different techniques.

Phonevision was to operate through a central unit in the community served. The center would receive special programs from a participating TV station by cable, would "scramble" the signals and return them to the station for transmission. The subscriber would receive a punched card to activate a decoding apparatus in his set to permit unscrambled reception. In the Subscriber-Vision method, customers likewise were to use punched cards, which would record the viewer's selection of programs for billing purposes.

Telemeter proposed a coin-box attached to the receiver; depositing a coin would activate the decoder for receiving each program. The Teleglobe scheme was to transmit the picture without scrambling, while sending the sound by wire for which the subscriber would pay a fee. Bi-Tran envisioned "piggy-backing" a pay program on the same TV channel as the normal free program, by a process called "contra-phase multiplexing."

That television could be a marvelous medium for education was recognized early in a 1953 series, Adventure. *Charles Collingwood guided listeners through the wonders of the American Museum of Natural History. Dr. George Gaylord Simpson (right) is shown explaining the skeletal structure of a prehistoric animal.*

Students of high schools and junior colleges throughout the country were permitted to express themselves publicly on important issues of the day on the CBS program, Youth Takes a Stand.

At New York University a college literature course telecast at the unheard-of hour of 6:30 in the morning proved surprisingly popular. In her Long Island living room, clad in a bathrobe, a young woman listens to the lecture. Upon payment of a registration fee to the University, she was entitled to a final examination at the end of the course and to academic credit if she passed.

These proposals kicked up a storm throughout the industry, with opposition led by the networks whose basic system of operation would be challenged. By 1958, more than 25,000 briefs had been filed in the FCC pay-TV proceedings. These filled over 75 volumes, the largest record of its kind in the Commission's history. Over a period of years, there were hearings before congressional committees and, in California, a popular referendum in which pay-TV was voted down.

The controversy did not involve pay TV for theatres or homes which employed common carrier or private cable facilities. "Closed circuit" (wired) programs, not being transmitted over the air, did not require FCC licensing. Eventually this proved to be the

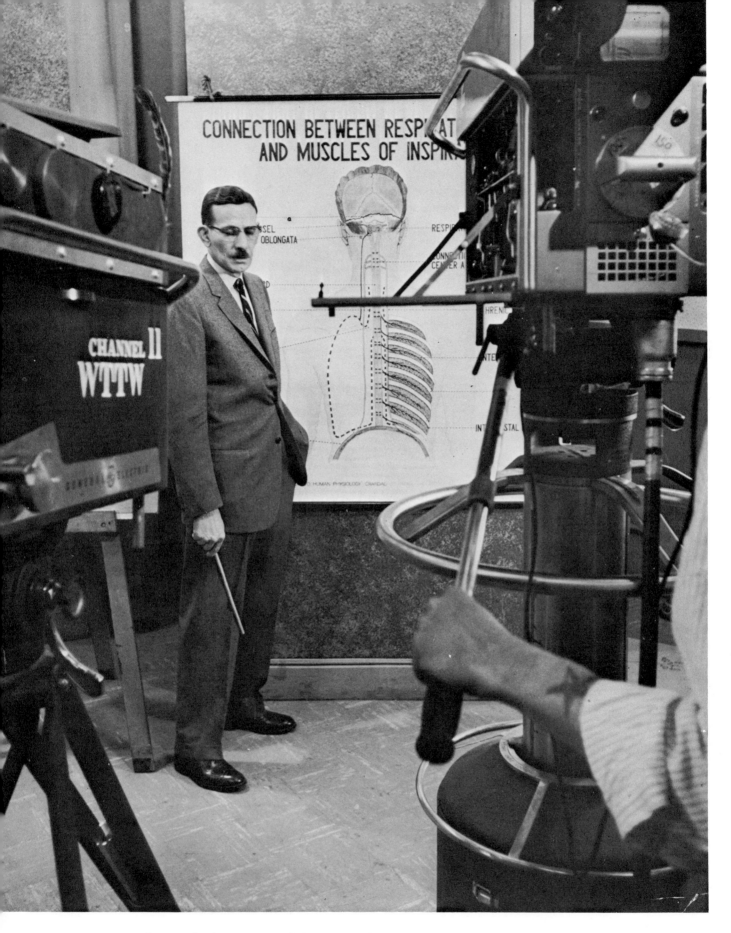

Educational television expanded on a broad scale throughout the United States, evolving gradually into a non-commercial network supported by endowments, listener contributions, or a combination of both. WTTW, Chicago, made history when it became the first TV station to offer a program of courses leading to a junior college degree. Samuel Howe is the teacher.

Chairman Nikita S. Khrushchev of the Soviet Union became a TV personality in October 1960 when he visited the United States for conferences with President Dwight D. Eisenhower and sessions at the United Nations. He is pictured above (center) with David Susskind (left) and an interpreter on the Open End *program.*

easier way: "cablevision" appeared in New York and other large cities. The subscriber paid a monthly fee for TV service by wire, assuring him of reception free from interference (an important advantage especially in color), and offering him first-run feature films, sporting events, or other programs not ordinarily available on the public air-waves.

As the decade ended, television was firmly established in American life as something more than entertainment, something more than a source of news. It had become a public utility rather than a luxury service, and a controlling influence on communications for better or worse.

5 .The Medium is the Message: The Sixties

In 1960 the Eisenhower era came to an abrupt end, not only in politics but in spirit. The American illusion of living in tranquillity amid a troubled world fell apart with the U-2 spy plane incident and the collapse of a U.S.-Soviet "summit conference." In Israel, Adolf Eichmann went on trial before television cameras that suddenly revived buried memories of the inhumanity of the Nazi scourge. During the same year, television took over a decisive role in the American electoral process.

The "Great Debates" between candidates John F. Kennedy and Richard M. Nixon went to the very heart of the relationship of broadcasting to democracy in the Space Age. They came about through the efforts of Dr. Frank Stanton, president of CBS, to set aside the "equal-time" rule, Section 315 of the Federal Communications Act. It required that if free time on the air were given to a candidate for public office, the station must grant equal time to *all* candidates for that office. In a presidential election, where there might be a dozen candidates of minor parties, equal time was impractical. For 1960 only, this rule was waived by a special Joint Resolution of Congress to permit the Kennedy-Nixon debates on TV.

More than 115 million citizens witnessed at least one of the face-to-face confrontations, carried on all three networks. Public opinion polls showed that voters "very much interested" in the outcome of the election increased from 45 per cent to 57 per cent after the debates, while the percentage of the electorate who voted rose from 60.4 per cent in 1956 to 64.5 per cent in 1960. How many voters made their choice between the candidates on the basis of what they saw on TV, no one knows, but the election was so close that the debates might well have been decisive. This much is known:

(1) Even prior to the debates, Senator Kennedy had won the Democratic nomination by a lavish use of local TV campaigning in state primaries. His turning point came in West Virginia where a major rival, Senator Hubert H. Humphrey, lacking Kennedy's finanncial resources for television time, went down to unexpected

Reality occasionally replaces illusion on the TV screen as illustrated by the trial of Adolf Eichmann, the Nazi officer executed for his part in the murder of European Jews during World War II. NBC correspondent Alvin Rosenfeld (right) is shown as he examines the documentation in the case in the Israeli archives in Jerusalem.

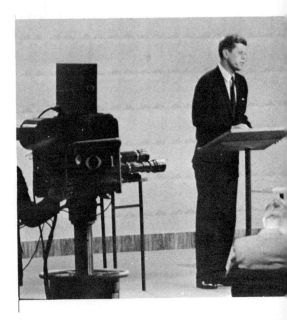

The Kennedy-Nixon debates were the highlight of the 1960 Presidential campaign. John F. Kennedy's election was widely attributed to his forensic superiority over Richard M. Nixon.

President John F. Kennedy brought a new poise to the television screen after he took office. He is pictured here at his first press conference in the White House.

Robert F. Kennedy was one of the key figures at the Democratic National Convention in Atlantic City in August, 1964. He pays a heartfelt tribute to his murdered brother in the TV picture. Four years later he, too, was dead.

defeat. (2) Of the two debaters, Vice President Nixon had been much the better known to the public because of his position; overnight the TV debates lifted Kennedy to equal prominence and wiped out the incumbent's advantage. (3) Nixon had campaigned personally in every one of the 50 States; with equal exposure on the air-waves all his physical exertion went for naught. (4) The *words* of the debaters evidently were of little consequence. Both men simply repeated their campaign arguments and slogans without adding anything new. (5) What counted was the *image* projected by the tube. Nixon looked heavy-jowled, exhausted, while Kennedy appeared fresh and vigorous, exuding confidence. Politicians took careful note of all these points; by 1968 the reshaping of national campaigns to fit television technique would be complete.

More and more in programming, television functioned as the mouthpiece of a nation. News and documentaries moved far ahead of drama in public attention and interest. During the political campaigns, CBS assigned a staff of 275 correspondents, reporters, and technicians, while NBC used a staff of more than 1,200 on election night. In its operation at the Republican convention, NBC required 150 full-time technicians, numbers of supervisors and subcontractors, 32 cameras, 90,000 pounds of technical gear, five mobile units, a camera-carrying Cadillac, and two mobile tape units. In contrast, the purely entertainment area of TV continued its descent from the creative peaks of the mid-Fifties.

Newton H. Minow

On May 9, 1961, President Kennedy's new chairman of the FCC, Newton H. Minow, a lawyer, assailed a meeting of the National Association of Broadcasters in Washington with open criticism . . . the famous "vast wasteland" speech. He challenged the 2,000 broadcasters to listen to their own stations:

> When television is good, nothing—not the theater, not the magazines or newspapers—nothing is better. But when television is bad, nothing is worse. I invite you to sit down in front of your television set when your station goes on the air and stay there without a book, magazine, newspaper, profit and loss sheet, or rating book to distract you and keep your eyes glued to that set until the station signs off. I can assure you that you will observe a vast wasteland.

You will see a procession of game shows, violence, audience participation shows, formula comedies about totally unbelievable families, blood and thunder, mayhem, violence, sadism, murder, Western badmen, Western good men, private eyes, gangsters, more violence, and cartoons. And, endlessly, commercials—many screaming, cajoling, and offending. And most of all, boredom. True, you will see a few things you will enjoy. But they will be very, very few. And if you think I exaggerate, try it.

This speech, though in fact a friendly tip to the broadcasters, was taken by them as an insult and a questioning of their integrity. Observers outside the industry went even further than Minow, such as one newspaper correspondent who said: "Television is not a vast wasteland. It is a jungle inhabited by pygmies." Minow's fire had been directed specifically at the effect of TV on children, and at the irresponsibility of many station owners. (Even when public service programs or superior children's material were produced by a network, they often were not carried by local stations.) Although the results were not immediately apparent, and Minow did not remain in office long enough to carry out his own plans for TV reform, his criticism unquestionably put the industry on its mettle and encouraged public support for better TV fare.

In another speech Minow said he had made a survey among ten- and twelve-year-olds in which he received the following reply to three questions asked:

President John F. Kennedy's inauguration in January, 1961, broadcast to the nation from the steps of the Capitol, included a stirring appeal for the help of the people.

Hubert H. Humphrey was nominated for President at the Democratic Convention in Chicago in August, 1968, after the collapse of the insurgent movement for Senator Eugene J. McCarthy. The screen shows the decisive roll-call vote.

The Democratic National Convention was disrupted by several nights of conflict between police and dissenting youths. TV audiences watched as Chicago police attacked with tear gas and hustled dissenters into a patrol wagon during the rioting.

Richard M. Nixon was nominated for President at the Republican National Convention at Miami Beach, Fla., in August, 1968. This was the moment on the TV when he clinched the nomination with the requisite number of delegate votes.

99 per cent preferred candy to spinach.

92 per cent preferred the movies to Sunday school.

79 per cent preferred to stay home and watch the game shows, soap operas, and cartoons on television rather than go to school.

Chairman Minow went on to say:

There is nothing wrong with giving these children some candy, in the form of television escape, but there is something wrong in not giving them some spinach, in the form of entertainment. And I have the feeling that most of us parents will send our children to Sunday school, even against their wishes; finally, even if we were tempted to keep our children home from public school to watch television, there are state laws backing up the principle that you just can't always give the children what they want.

His conclusion to the "wasteland" speech set the tone for the Kennedy Administration: "It is not enough to cater to the nation's

Pope Paul VI paid his first visit to the U. S. in 1965 in connection with the ecumenical movement. He greets the nation on his arrival at John F. Kennedy airport; U. N. Secretary General U Thant and Governor Nelson Rockefeller of New York are on the right.

whims—you must also serve the nation's needs. The squandering of our airwaves is no less important than the lavish waste of any precious natural resource."

The years that followed were among the most dramatic— and at times disastrous—in the nation's history. Television reacted by developing two styles: frequent special one-time programs of high quality entertainment, as pioneered in the mid-Fifties; and ever more intensive documenting of the world as it really is. The two techniques often overlapped. Historian Daniel J. Boorstin, writing in *Look Magazine* in 1968, observed this phenomenon as follows:

Now, political information and campaign propaganda come in constantly flowing streams . . . into at least 93 per cent of American homes . . . The broadcasting flow brings all points of view into everybody's living room. People become tolerant of

The "spirit of Glassboro" was born in the small New Jersey town in June, 1967 as a harbinger of improved relations between the U. S. and the Soviet Union. President Johnson and Premier Aleksei Kosygin are shown with their heads together before the microphones.

personalities and ideas that have some entertainment value, even if they hate the personalities and ideas and don't want to be persuaded. The whole spectrum of differing views now intrudes itself. Now, you actually have to turn the channel to send the unwanted spokesman away! . . .

The very nature of TV offers a new national forum for spokesmen of unpopular views. New forms, like the vastly popular interview and conversation shows of David Susskind, Johnny Carson, Joey Bishop, and others give these new minorities a new voice, a vivid image, and network time they could never afford to buy. The more violent their point of view or their personality, the more apt they are to be considered "newsworthy." Zany ideas, preferably expressed by zany people, have surefire appeal. They liven up the show, raise the Nielsen ratings—and make national celebrities out of political oddballs. No view is too marginal, no political slogan too outrageous to be denied its moment on the center of the stage. The network flow brings Democratic candidates into the homes of diehard Republicans and Republican candidates into the homes of diehard Democrats, but it also brings into everybody's home both George Wallace and Stokely Carmichael.

Television and the news

With each year that passed, the medium literally immersed

Bitter conflict between the police and youthful dissenters in the streets of Chicago marred the Democratic National Convention in August, 1968. Television coverage of the disorders created a national issue. Mayor Richard Daley explains the city's position to CBS "anchor man" Walter Cronkite, who had been critical of police roughing of the press.

the American people in their own history. Millions witnessed deeds on their television screens that were both fascinating and repellent. Never before had so many people been, in effect, at the scene of an actual murder. Never before had such a huge audience been so emotionally engaged at the tragic funerals of three assassinated leaders. Never before in the recorded history of man on earth had the non-combatant millions observed at close hand actual combat in a war.

To be an eye and ear witness of a Jack Ruby appearing out of a crowd to send a bullet into the abdomen of Lee Harvey Oswald, to be present at the funeral procession of President Kennedy and hear the muffled drums and see a child's salute, to be in a church listening to the recorded voice of Martin Luther King predicting his own assassination while he lay dead in a coffin—these were "messages" of such devastating impact as to be almost unbearable to watch.

Vivid as were the radio broadcasts of Edward R. Murrow during the bombings of London in World War II, none could compare with the horror of watching a South Vietnamese officer walk up to a bound and captured Viet Cong prisoner, put a gun to the man's head and pull the trigger. This was television telling us the way things really were. It was news reporting of the highest

Lee Harvey Oswald, arrested within a few hours of the assassination of President John F. Kennedy in Dallas in 1963, is shown on TV with a deputy sheriff in the Dallas jail seconds before he was murdered by Jack Ruby.

order, and more: it was social commentary that changed the way men think.

The Space Age

Not all the news was bad. In 1961 the Russian Yuri Gagarin became the first man to travel beyond the earth's atmosphere into space, followed within a month by the American Alan B. Shepard, Jr. Television kept its eye on space, culminating in 1965 with views of men actually "walking" in the gravity-less firmament, and with astounding photographs of the surface of the moon and of the planet Mars. By 1969 the Apollo missions to the moon were able to transmit everything they saw—including close-ups of moon craters and incredibly awesome views of the planet earth—to set-watchers in their homes, live and in color.

After the assassination of President John F. Kennedy, Lee Harvey Oswald was fatally shot by Jack Ruby in the basement of the Dallas jail, in full view of a TV audience of millions. Ruby is shown above being overpowered by law officers an instant later as the dying Oswald slumps to the floor.

The state funeral of President John F. Kennedy brought dignitaries from all over the world to Washington to pay their tribute to the fallen leader. Here Mrs. Kennedy, flanked by Robert and Edward Kennedy, marches stoically in the funeral procession.

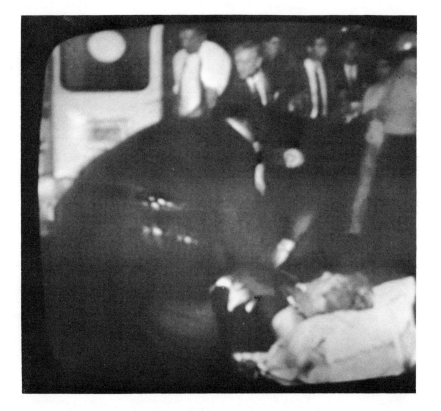

The murder of Senator Robert F. Kennedy in a Los Angeles hotel at the onset of the Presidential campaign in June, 1968, was the third assassination covered by TV in the past five years. Here the stricken candidate's head is cradled on a pillow while awaiting transfer to a hosptial where he died.

This cosmic drama was played against an obbligato of murder in the Congo, the erection of the Berlin wall, the Bay of Pigs fiasco in Cuba, and a near-nuclear war over the presence of Soviet missile bases in Castro's now avowedly Communist land. Thanks to television, people today recall recent history in political vignettes: the space capsules splashing down from orbit; Krushchev at the United Nations banging a desk with his shoe; President Kennedy appealing to the students at the University of Mississippi to accept the admission of a Negro; the wedding of Princess Margaret of England; the funeral of Winston Churchill; the burning of Detroit; the agony in a Los Angeles hotel kitchen when Bobby Kennedy was shot; rioting at the Chicago Democratic Convention and on the campus of Columbia University.

The assassination of Dr. Martin Luther King in Memphis, Tennessee, in April, 1968 was another epic tragedy in television coverage. His widow, his children, and his brother are shown here at the funeral march in Atlanta, Georgia.

157

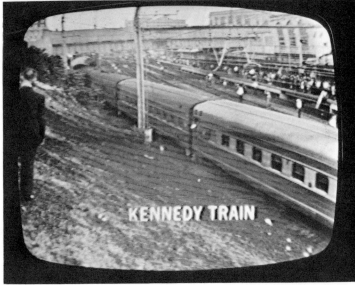

Senator Edward Kennedy delivering his poignant eulogy at his brother Robert's funeral.

The body of Senator Robert F. Kennedy was transported by train to Washington for burial in Arlington National Cemetery following the funeral in New York. Thousands flocked to stations along the way to pay their last respects.

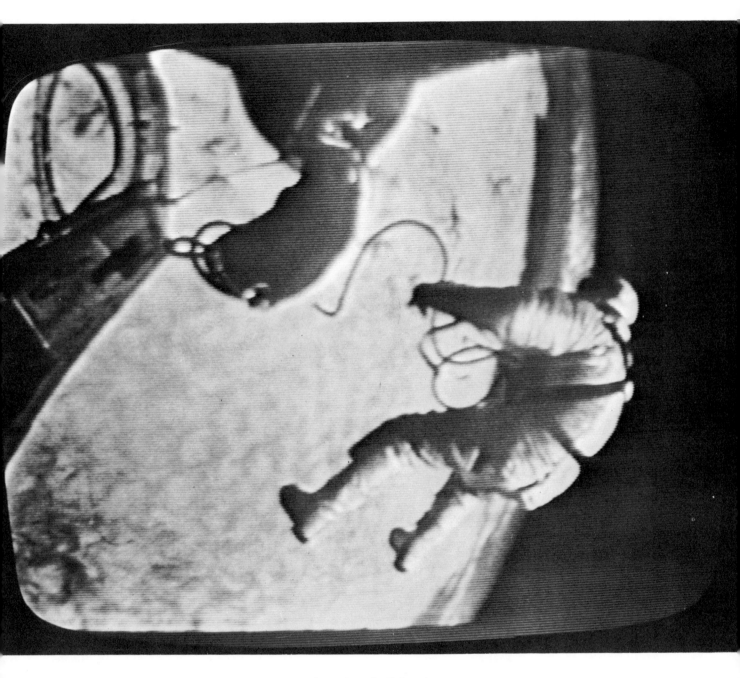

Among the manned flights into orbit that of Gemini 4 in June, 1965, was the most spectacular. Lt. Col. Edward H. White became the first American and the second human to "walk" in space. He later died in a flash-fire aboard the Apollo spaceship at Cape Kennedy, Fla. Note that this picture can be turned any way you like: there is no "up" or "down" in space.

The Huntley-Brinkley team won the Emmy Award in 1960 as television's top news program and NBC produced three new public affairs series. It also presented some 150 special shows, including such productions as *Macbeth,* several operas, *Our American Heritage,* and revivals of *Peter Pan* and *Fred Astaire Time.* CBS opened the year with *The Fabulous Fifties,* with Julie Andrews, Shelley Berman, Betty Comden and Adolph Green, Jackie Gleason, Rex Harrison, Mike Nichols and Elaine May, Eric Sevareid, and Dick Van Dyke. Later in the year Danny Kaye appeared in his

Unbelievably, the eye of television reached beyond the confines of Planet Earth in 1964–1965 when as part of the exploration of space, the U.S. series of Ranger probes returned thousands of close-up photos of the Moon before impacting on its surface. Ranger 9 sent back this first live TV picture in March, 1965.

first TV entertainment special. Such was to become the programming pattern. CBS presented an unprecedented total of 765 hours of news and public affairs, including *CBS Reports, Eye-witness to History, Face the Nation,* and *Twentieth Century.* The statistics of other network programming showed a similar trend.

Color TV boom

Color television, after a slow start in the Fifties, entered a boom phase with NBC carrying over 1,000 hours of color broadcasts. This grew to 2,000 hours in 1962—more than the total of American color motion pictures produced in the previous eight years. In 1965 broadcasts in color exploded over all the prime listening hours. ABC increased its color programming of evening shows to 50 per cent. CBS added color to many of its special broadcasts, and NBC began to use the phrase, "The Full Color Network." By year's end 96 per cent of its nighttime schedule was in color, along with all major programs, sports events, and specials. Some 2.7 million color TV sets were sold, more than twice as many as in 1964—and a huge number in view of prices ranging from $500 per set to $1,000 and more.

The most popular entertainers continued to be the old standbys who had established themselves in the Fifties. Innovations were few, except that *Sing Along With Mitch* (Miller) was one of the big hits of 1961, while a new drama series, *The Defenders,* received an Associated Press citation as the year's best. Created by Reginald Rose in the spirit of television's Golden Age, it began a cycle of problem-play shows which had more substance to them than most "action" or crime tales on TV.

Specials and documentaries

The big dramatic event of the year was a two-hour broadcast of Grahame Greene's *The Power and the Glory,* starring Sir Laurence Olivier. Other major shows were vehicles for Ingrid Bergman, Julie Harris, E. G. Marshall, Jo Van Fleet, and Mildred Dunnock. In lighter vein, Jack Benny played a concert at Carnegie Hall, Arthur Godfrey gave a travelogue, and Jackie Gleason played in *The Million Dollar Incident.* The combination of a well-known personality with an offbeat subject could be counted upon to attract

Mitch Miller proved that a simple songfest can be a hit on the air when he inaugurated Sing Along with Mitch *in 1960.*

The Defenders *brought a refreshingly sympathetic treatment to the problems of the accused caught in the coils of the law beginning in 1961. E. G. Marshall, the chief defender, faces the jury here in a typical courtroom scene.*

161

Bill Cosby made television history in 1965 when he became the first Negro to be cast as a co-star in a continuing melodrama, I Spy, *with Robert Culp. Subsequently, he starred in the* Bill Cosby Special *in 1968 in which he visited a band of youngsters in his hometown of Philadelphia.*

the increasingly blasé listener.

In the documentary field, CBS scored an important beat when it received permission from the White House to produce a full-hour tour of the presidential mansion with Mrs. John F. Kennedy as hostess. The success of this taped telecast would be the signal for a number of other "tours" with famous people in famous buildings or sites elsewhere in the world, such as Elizabeth Taylor in London. Fortunately for television, its documenting of history kept establishing the value of the medium as an integral part of American life, and so diverting criticism from its weaker segments. In January 1962, CBS found it necessary to testify at FCC public hearings that government regulation, "suggested by some as the road to improved programs, is illusory and dangerous." The network advanced the view "that the future of television will be most promising if the medium continues to derive its impetus from a free competition for the attention and approval of the public." Much of the intellectual and social-minded community disagreed.

International TV

Electronic communications took a great leap forward in July 1962 with the launching of the Telstar and Relay satellites. By using the orbiting stations as an active relay for signals, Americans and Europeans for the first time were able to share the sight of a live television picture as it spanned the Atlantic. The first trans-oceanic broadcast via Telstar originated at the BBC transmitting station at Geonhilly Down, Cornwall, England, and was picked up by CBS. Later, all three U. S. networks united with the 17-nation European Broadcasting Union in the first formal exchange of bi-continental TV.

Now more TV time than ever was being devoted to the quickening pace of news events around the world. It became habitual for the networks to interrupt and preempt regular TV programs to keep the public abreast of these developments. During the week of the Cuban crisis, for example, ABC preempted six hours for news reports. CBS did ten hours of uninterrupted reporting of John Glenn's successful vault through space. Invariably, it was television's specials based upon news or history that caused the most widespread comment among listeners and in the press.

Bob Hope, who has traveled the world over entertaining troups, is one of television's outstanding comedians. Here he is shown with Dean Martin in a Bob Hope special, in 1963.

In a memorable special, Mrs. John F. Kennedy took CBS correspondent Charles Collingwood and the nation on a tour of the White House that she and a Fine Arts committee had redecorated with authentic American furnishings.

The tempestuous Elizabeth Taylor toured London in 1963 for TV. Here she is on the banks of the Thames.

Examples of these on CBS were *Eisenhower on the Presidency;* a biography of Frank Lloyd Wright; and *Washington Conversation,* an interview with Senator Carl Hayden of Arizona marking his 50th year in office. ABC won an award for *Meet Comrade Student,* a program on its *Close-Up* series. NBC on *Project 20* offered *He Is Risen,* a sequel to the award-winning *The Coming of Christ; Circus,* narrated by Emmett Kelly the clown; and a history of crime in America narrated by Edward G. Robinson. Other NBC specials were *The Ordeal of Woodrow Wilson, The Beauty of Women* from Venus de Milo to Elizabeth Taylor, and a biography of Robert E. Lee.

Godfrey Cambridge was one of the first Negro comedians to employ wit and satire to advance the civil rights cause. He strikes a characteristic gesture in this appearance on a Jack Paar special in 1965.

Bob Hope has been the perennial master of ceremonies on the film industry's Oscar Awards Show. Here he is with Marlon Brando who won for his performance in "On the Waterfront" in 1954.

Julie Andrews and Carol Burnett staged a two-woman spectacular called Julie and Carol at Carnegie Hall *in 1962 and brought the house down with their antics.*

The irrepressible Judy Garland captured the hearts of her admirers with her singing in the Judy Garland Special *in 1962. She enlisted such seasoned performers as Dean Martin and Frank Sinatra as her guests.*

The 18th Olympic Games in Tokyo in the summer of 1964 were televised to the U.S. and around the world via satellite.

This type of programming had originated on educational stations such as those affiliated with universities. The commercial broadcasters were able to apply to it infinitely greater technical and financial resources. What would be merely a lecture on an educational station would become on networks an on-location development of the theme in scene and action, expertly enacted and narrated. Television was finding a way to "educate" in the guise of reporting the wonders of the world as entertainment.

Films move in

Meanwhile in entertainment as such the networks were running a neck-and-neck race to avoid being original. Not that programs weren't individually funny or dramatic; they were all cut from the same cloth. Thus if NBC had its *Dr. Kildare,* ABC had its *Ben*

The funeral of Sir Winston Churchill in London was relayed to the U.S. by Telstar in January, 1965.

The Telstar satellite or "switchboard in the sky" was inaugurated in July, 1962 as a history-making device to transmit live news events across the Atlantic. Richard Dimbleby, ace BBC commentator, is shown as his picture was received in New York.

The Beverly Hillbillies *astoundingly jumped to the top of the ratings when it was introduced in 1962. As members of the Clampett clan who overwhelmed Beverly Hills with their newfound wealth, Buddy Ebsen as Jed (left), Max Baer, Donna Douglas, and Irene Ryan, riding shotgun, roll through the streets in triumph.*

The Man From U.N.C.L.E. *opened in 1964 as a serious attempt at an espionage show, but it had its lighter moments. David McCallum (left), and Robert Vaughn (seen here with Susan Silo) cook up a strategem to foil their enemies from THRUSH.*

Casey. If ABC had its *Breaking Point,* NBC had its *The Eleventh Hour.* What might be called ping-pong programming ("What you can do, I can do better") could have continued indefinitely but for two breakthroughs. One was *Saturday Night at the Movies* on NBC, the first network to inaugurate a regular movie night in prime listening time. Beginning in September 1961, it proved so successful that NBC added another weekly movie night in 1963, and the other networks followed suit. Thte effect of this was to boost the price of first-run Hollywood films to $800,000 or more for two or three TV showings, while drying up the source of films for non-

Get Smart *went on the air in 1965 as a satirical reaction against the flood of secret agent capers. Don Adams (left), Dick Gautier and Barbara Feldon starred.*

network, local stations. The latter were reduced to showing available epics over and over again. In 1968 it was estimated that *Stage Coach, The Long Voyage Home,* and *Foreign Correspondent* had each been sold to every TV station in New York City and had each been shown at least 75 times.

The second breakthrough was "camp"—something so outrageously bad that it passed as clever farce. *The Beverly Hillbillies,* first presented in 1962 on CBS, instantly became a synonym for the low estate of television comedy. A comic-strip-like yarn about innocent bumpkins who strike it rich and outwit the city slickers of Beverly Hills (a pretentious suburb of Hollywood, California), this oafish tale created a sensation, actually out-rating *The Lucy Show* as top program of the year. The same tongue-in-cheek vein created the cops-and-robbers spoof (*Car 54, Where Are You?*), the

The comic strip Batman *was brought to TV in 1966 and achieved instantaneous success with its purposely exaggerated feats of derring-do. Adam West as the lead is either funny or fantastic, depending on the viewer.*

Fred Gwynne (left) and Joe E. Ross represented the law in Car 54, Where Are You?

spy spoof (*Get Smart!, The Man from U.N.C.L.E.*), and ultimately the spoof of spoofs, *Batman.* This last was out of comic books read by children in the Thirties, offered anew to those same children grown to adulthood, and in the strange, mocking mood of the late Sixties, hailed by them as a "camp" masterpiece.

The death of a President

Whatever else the networks thought they were doing, they could not be faulted for profitability. All three had record sales and income in 1962, the highest in the history of both radio and TV. The nation, too, was settling into a rather comfortable feeling about itself, hopeful that its youthful and energetic President would find solutions to the many foreign and domestic problems and, especially, would show young people the way to future greatness. Then, suddenly, one black weekend in 1963, America's optimism was smashed and the nation headed into what historian Arnold Toynbee might call a "time of troubles."

At 1:40 P.M. Eastern Standard Time on Friday, November 22, Walter Cronkite broke into the CBS network soap opera, *As the World Turns,* to announce that President John F. Kennedy had been shot by a sniper in Dallas, Texas. That was probably the earliest television bulletin, although radio news flashes no doubt preceded it. The two media thereby demonstrated their differing functions; radio announces a news event and nothing is faster, but television *partakes* of the news as it unfolds. In the crisis it was to television that the public instinctively turned for the "real" story. For the next three and a half days Cronkite and his CBS associates devoted themselves to the longest uninterrupted news report in the history of broadcasting. Nearly 700 people worked steadily, often around the clock, during the "four dark days" of the assassination and its aftermath. The reports were relayed to Europe by satellite, and jet aircraft carried film to 38 other countries.

NBC-TV devoted 71½ hours to the Kennedy tragedy. More than 400 newsmen and technicians in 33 mobile units were deployed across the country as the story developed in Dallas, Washington, and other key points. ABC news coverage was a continuous 60 hours over television, including numerous special programs. A tribute to President Kennedy featured such artists as Frederic March, Marian Anderson, Charlton Heston, Jerome Hines, and

The Beatles created a new life style as well as a musical idiom for the younger set in appearances on the Ed Sullivan Show *and other shows. Paul McCartney, Ringo Starr, John Lennon, and George Harrison (left to right) cavort as members of a village band in the Austrian Alps in the movie "Help" broadcast on TV.*

Isaac Stern, with commentary by Edward P. Morgan and Howard K. Smith. When the mournful strains of "Taps" echoed across the field of Arlington Cemetery on Monday, they were heard simultaneously via satellite in 23 countries with a combined population of more than 600 million. NBC provided facilities for eight European reporters in New York, enabling them to broadcast a description of the Kennedy funeral in their native languages.

This tragic loss of a leader, a turning-point in recent American history, had certain side effects on television itself. For the first time, the intrusion of the TV camera into real life became evident; it ceased to be merely an observer of events and became a participant. The killing of Lee Harvey Oswald, the accused assassin, before he could be questioned or tried, might have been avoided if Oswald had been spirited secretly from one Dallas jail to another. Instead he was paraded before the television cameras—precisely, it appears, to accommodate the medium—and in the resultant confusion an armed outsider, Jack Ruby, was able to penetrate police security lines. Ruby's fatal shooting of Oswald took place in full view of the TV audience; it was automatically taped for instant replay, and replayed again and again until assuredly few people in the entire world could have failed to see it.

Television also intruded at the moment of swearing in Lyndon B. Johnson as President aboard the jet plane, Air Force One, in the presence of Mrs. Kennedy. Again it seemed as if the circumstances were cut to fit the camera, at a cost in personal feelings and political disunity which was to plague Mr. Johnson throughout his term of office. Bar associations and courts reexamined the rights of the press —now including television—in covering judicial proceedings. Political leaders became increasingly wary of being trapped into off-the-cuff statements for the camera at legislative hearings or conventions. President Johnson, for example, found it expedient to call press conferences at unscheduled hours, thus choosing the times when he would or wouldn't be at the mercy of the television eye.

Race and revolution

In 1964 three civil rights workers were murdered by white racists in Mississippi. It appeared that the Kennedy assassination had uncovered a latent streak of violence in the American character, and TV reflected it. With the passage of the Civil Rights Act of

The civil disorders in Watts, Newark, Detroit, and other cities in the mid-Sixties were among the most dramatic news events covered by the networks. Daniel P. Moynihan (right), then director of the MIT-Harvard Joint Center for Urban Studies, and NBC correspondent Bill Matney survey the wreckage in Detroit.

175

1964, non-violent demonstrations by Negroes in Southern towns and cities such as Selma and Montgomery, Alabama, led by the Rev. Martin Luther King, gradually were transformed into street riots in Northern cities. The burning and looting of Watts, a black neighborhood of Los Angeles, shocked the nation in 1965. During the next few summers the ghettos became seething cauldrons, boiling and erupting successively in Detroit, Newark, Chicago, and Washington itself. All of these troublous episodes were covered by television, which, in addition, endeavored to explain what was happening. Fair as the explanations might be, they tended to satisfy no one. While advocates of Black Power became ever more militant, white ethnic groups became ever more resentful. TV cameramen in

That Was the Week That Was, imported from England in 1964 as an irreverent take-off on current events and contemporary personalities, started with a bang, but never quite caught on. David Frost (left), who was a fixture in the London version, Elliot Reed, and Nancy Ames, the "TW3 Girl," lampoon a headline in the news.

The Smothers Brothers Comedy Hour proved to be an instant hit when it premiered in 1965 with its free-swinging, nonconformist approach to topical subjects. Tom (left) and Dick Smothers finger their instruments a critical ditty on some current problem.

some instances were accused of instigating provocative acts to "make a story."

TV documentaries also explored the rest of the seething world in ever-widening horizons. NBC filmed *Profile of Communism* and *The Kremlin,* the latter a history in color of Russian art treasures. The network's outstanding triumph was *The Tunnel,* filming the actual escape of refugees from East Germany by tunneling under the Berlin wall, which won eleven awards. ABC, now employing its own newsreel film crews, produced *Saga of Western Man,* a four-part series on significant periods in history, and a TV adaptation of Theodore White's *The Making of the President,* the 1960 campaign. Coverage of sports also became world-wide on ABC.

The excellence of public affairs programming in the mid-Sixties is self-evident from a sample listing for 1963 as, on CBS: *The Roots of Freedom, The Law and Lee Oswald, Dialogues of Allan Nevins and Henry Steele Commager, Ten Years After Stalin:* and on ABC: *The Soviet Woman, The Day That Life Begins* (a sensitive presentation of birth). A fictional series, *East Side/West Side,* starring George C. Scott, was attempted with topical social problems as plot material. Its short life indicated that television now was split down the middle—half real life, half drama or variety—and the two halves were not always compatible.

Shirley Booth (shown here with Frank Gifford) proved what a fine actress can do with a mediocre script when she opened in 1961 in Hazel, *modeled on the Saturday Evening Post cartoons about a housemaid.*

Bonanza went on view in 1959 and became the highest-rated show in all television for many years. Here Lorne Greene, as Ben Cartright, and Dan Blocker, as his loyal son Hoss, protect an army payroll from bandits.

BLAIR HOSPITAL
EMERGENCY

Dr. Kildare was the first and perhaps the most successful of a series of medical dramas that began in 1961. The veteran "doctor" Raymond Massey and the neophyte Richard Chamberlain starred.

Trends in TV drama

The dramatic segment continued to be dominated by routine shows; the television playwrights' problem seemed to be that of finding new occupations to write about. For example, *Mr. Novak* was a full hour series centered on an American high school, excellently acted by Dean Jagger and James Franciscus. In one valiant try, the *Richard Boone Show* introduced repertory theater with some fine original dramas. But even Mr. Boone, who had been propelled to fame as *Medic* and as Paladin in *Have Gun, Will Travel,* found such material too rich for the audience. With the demise of this show, television drama reverted to adaptations of stage plays or vanished altogether in favor of full-length films.

In variety, an interesting innovation was *That Was the Week That Was.* An import from England, it lampooned people and events in the current news, and it came to American television like a breath of fresh air. The opening program drew over 10,000 letters and telegrams. Unfortunately, in American hands "TW3" became heavy-handed rather than sophisticated in its satire, or futilely pursued the mass appeal of broad comedy. Echoes of it, however, persisted as a target for future topical comedy and variety shows, such as *The Smothers Brothers,* the *Rowan and Martin Laugh-In,* and Carol Burnett. "TW3" opened the door to a revolution in entertainment, a result of America's looking at itself with a candid eye, in no hurry to censor out the truth of what it saw.

Again in 1964 the state of the art is well described by listing a few of the most successful shows. New on NBC were *The Rogues,* starring David Niven, Charles Boyer, and Gig Young as jet-set confidence men; *The Man From U.N.C.L.E.,* starring Robert Vaughn as a suave secret agent who out-Bonds James Bond, and making a star of his straight man, played by David McCallum; and *Flipper,* the adventures of a pet porpoise. Returning top-rated shows that year were *Bonanza,* the No. 1 program; *Mr. Novak; The Virginian,* a 90-minute Western; *Hazel,* the improbable maid played by Shirley Booth; *Dr. Kildare; Kraft Suspense Theater;* and *The Bob Hope Chrysler Theater,* the latter two consisting of drama adaptations.

The CBS contribution to novelty was *Gomer Pyle, USMC* (for some reason military and war backgrounds had become a fashionable setting for humor); *The Munsters,* a spoof on horror films; and *Gilligan's Island.* Returnees were *The Beverly Hillbillies;* the *Andy Griffith Show; My Favorite Martian* (comic science fiction); *Petticoat Junction; Lassie; The Lucy Show;* and the *Dick Van Dyke Show,* which after a slow start in 1961 had emerged as one of the most consistently funny, well-written, and well-played comedy series on the air.

Gomer Pyle, U.S.M.C. *told the story of the tribulations of an awkward recruit in the Marines. Jim Nabors played Gomer.*

The Munsters *mirrored the taste of the times by making horror laughable and lovable in a 1964 show. Al Lewis (left), Fred Gwynne and Yvonne DeCarlo make up this mad scene.*

Bewitched was one of the weirdest and most captivating shows to appear on the screen in 1964. Elizabeth Montgomery played Samantha the lovely witch and Dick York her human husband.

Frank Sinatra from a TV special A Man and his Music, *in 1967.*

ABC scored a breakthrough of sorts with *Peyton Place,* a soap opera switched from daytime to nighttime, based on a highly sensational and sexy novel. It marked a permanent departure from old fashioned standards of morality. By 1968, *Variety* could report:

> The daytime soaps, revelling in the devastation of taboos, have already done nymphomania, abortion, homosexuality, frigidity, and miscegenation, and one of them recently has been fooling around with incest. . . .*Peyton Place,* which had seemed so over-sexed when it premiered four years ago, looks mild in retrospect.

By 1968, as a matter of fact, such "scandalous," "racy," or "adult" films as *The Pink Panther* with Peter Sellers, *Never On Sunday* with Melina Mercouri, *The Apartment* with Jack Lemmon and Shirley MacLaine, and the Italian sensation, *La Dolce Vita,* had been aired with very little fuss. This placed television only three or four years behind the films and the stage in a social revolution that, in the Sixties, would wipe out moral barriers as old as the Protestant Reformation.

Other new ABC shows in 1964 were *The Addams Family, Voyage to the Bottom of the Sea, No Time for Sergeants,* and *Bewitched,* which proved to be an off-beat comedy starring Elizabeth Montgomery and Dick York. Successful returnees on this network were *Ben Casey, Combat, The Fugitive, Ozzie and Harriet, McHale's Navy, Patty Duke, My Three Sons, Donna Reed,* and *The Flintstones,* a sophisticated cartoon.

Some of the specials of the year were *Once Upon a Mattress,* a 90-minute version of the stage musical starring Carol Burnett; *An Hour With Robert Goulet;* a performance of the Royal Ballet in London's Covent Garden; a feature on Winston Churchill's paintings; *The Louvre,* in color; *The Red, White, and Blue,* an NBC pictorial hymn to patriotism which drew a huge mail response; and *Letters From Vietnam,* the revelation of ABC correspondent John Scali's secret contact by a Soviet representative, during the 1962 Cuban missile crisis, to convey Moscow's willingness to compromise.

Growth of the industry

Throughout the country there was a steady growth of multiple set ownership, estimated in 1965 at 20 per cent of all television families, with the likelihood of increasing to three out of every four homes by 1975. Profits of the networks continued their upward course. CBS began to call itself "the world's largest advertising medium," NBC said it "attracted more national advertisers than any other network," and ABC confessed that it held "the leading position in the field of televised sports." They began seeking new fields to conquer. Both ABC and CBS constructed new office buildings in New York, 40 and 38 stories high, respectively. NBC through its merchandising division entered into various associations with book publishers, toy and game companies, clothing, and even a special kind of Western bread company. In show business the television tail had long since been wagging the Broadway-Hollywood dog. CBS, for example, owned *My Fair Lady* and reveled in the huge profits of being a successful "angel." Then they bought the New York Yankees, giving rise to suspicion that American professional sports thenceforth would be designed to display beer and automobile commercials rather than athletic prowess.

In each year the networks managed to come up with at least one program of sufficient interest to halt the drift of jaded listeners to some other form of leisure activity, and to get the public talking again about television. In 1965 it was Barbra Streisand, star of *Funny Girl*, in a special for CBS; and Frank Sinatra and Julie Andrews in similar big shows for NBC. A major innovation on CBS was *The National Drivers Test,* which involved the audience in an examination of their own skills as automobile drivers. The response was so favorable that the test was repeated in revised form a year later, also a *National Citizenship Test* which questioned Americans about their rights and duties as citizens.

All three networks in 1966 passed the half-billion dollar level in revenues, with CBS exceeding $800 million. The latter network consisted of 248 radio and 255 television stations, while ABC had 138 primary affiliated TV stations providing direct coverage to 93 per cent of U.S. television homes. NBC became the first "full color network" by converting its entire line-up of programs to color, carried throughout the country.

Color created new opportunities for "production numbers," such as the Miss America pageant, or an original musical version of *Alice Through the Looking Glass* with an all-star cast. It also introduced the block-buster movie. An ABC showing of *The Bridge on the River Kwai* in full, with minimum interruptions for com-

The Miss America Pageant *in Atlantic City has been an annual TV spectacular since 1954, with the antics of Bert Parks as master of ceremonies frequently overshadowing the winners. This is Judith Anne Ford, 18, of Belvedere, Ill. who won the 1968 contest as Miss America of 1969.*

181

Barbra Streisand conquered television in 1965 with her gamin appeal in the one-woman spectacular My Name Is Barbara.

mercials by the sponsor, Ford Motor Company, attracted the largest TV audience of the year, next to the Academy Awards annual presentation.

The commercials

Beginning in 1959 the advertising business annually awarded statuettes called Clios, roughly equivalent to Oscars in the Hollywood world, to winning entries in the American Television and Radio Commercials Festival. Many television buffs in the Sixties were insisting that the commercials displayed greater creative talent than the shows which were supposed to carry them. The following is extracted from a review of the 1968 ATRC Festival by Joan Walker in the New York *Times:*

> The length of commercials, of course, is in their favor. If you don't like the star or the music, just sit there for two minutes

at the most and it will all be over.

The music, for the most part, is just as good as movie music or the sound tracks on the television shows themselves. "The Girl Watchers Theme" that Pepsi-Cola uses is just as catchy as "Talk to the Animals." You're a lot more likely to find yourself singing about that "silly millimeter longer" or how "Pan Am makes the going great" than "The Champion of the Western World" from "High Chaparral," which got an Emmy nomination. "Only Mustang makes it happen/Only Mustang has the key" is a pretty good number too.

Commercials are, heaven knows, star-studded. Just a partial list of the festival's stars would include Paul Ford, Godfrey Cambridge, Vice President and Mrs. Hubert H. Humphrey, Lou Jacobi, Howard Morris, Enid Markey, Jack Klugman, David Wayne, Jose Ferrer, Joel Grey, Jack Gilford, Martin Balsam, Edmund O'Brien, Dane Clark, George Matthews, Barry Sullivan, Joey Heatherton, Petula Clark, and Herschel Bernardi. (Bernardi, in advertising circles, is not known as a Broadway actor; he is introduced as "one of the busiest and best voiceovers around— the voice of the Jolly Green Giant and Charley the Tuna!")

The level of humor is high. The pitch for the movie "Luv"— ("Hey, let's hear it for the mature audience") was funny. Jack Gilford's pantomime performances for Cracker Jack are usually funny in a bittersweet way. "Your grocer has volunteered to accept money for Utica Club beer" is a good line. Stan Freberg's commercial for Jeno's frozen pizza rolls, "Show Us Your Pizza Roll Pack"—a satire on the Lark campaign that stars Clayton Moore, Jay Silverheels, and a cast of 52—is hilarious. It won Clio's in two categories—"Confections, Snacks" and "Best Use of Humor"—and was apparently the sentimental favorite and popular choice, because its winning was greeted with cheers, whistles and wild applause.

The Medaglia d'Oro 60-second domestic situation comedy ("It's your wife—Doris!") is better than most half-hour shows in the same genre. And there is a 15-second Ban deodorant spot that brought the house down. You know the one: She says, "If I change to Ban roll-on deodorant, will my dream come true?" and he says, "I don't know, but mine will." Now that's as funny as any blackout on *Rowan and Martin's Laugh-in.*

Foreign commercials are more fun to look at than domestic ones. There is even a good one for a detergent. With the possible exception of the occasions when Wally Cox used to go diffidently down into his basement laundry room with his big box of Salvo, there had never been a good detergent commercial. But the office of Young and Rubicam in Frankfort, Germany, turned out a dilly for Dash, in which the inhabitants of a quaint German village stand on the cobblestones and wave their clean white tablecloths at the Dash aviator up in his helicopter. The Japanese use children a great deal—children running, washing, rolling around with dachshunds—and they use them with as much impact as Francis Thompson and Alexander Hammid would. The French have done a 75-second color film for Larousse's "Journal d'Année" that is a technical triumph. When was the last time you saw a good commercial for a book in this country?

Some foreign countries come to the rescue of the viewers with rules and regulations that our Federal Communications Commission might consider. The Canadian Broadcasting Corporation, for instance, does not allow any commercials for deodorants, toilet paper, or toilet bowl cleaners. In Italy, the product cannot be mentioned until the last 15 seconds of a two-minute message. The result: The commercials are almost non-commercial and sometimes charming, suspenseful, plotty vignettes that have you on the edge of your seat guessing what the name of the product is going to be.

There are fascinating little tidbits that can be picked up at a commercials festival. It wasn't all roses. There was one commercial,

Jack Paar (right) was the host of The Morning Show *when this picture with baritone Dick Sommers was taken in 1955.*

Later, Paar went on to extraordinary fame when he took over the Tonight *show in 1957 (soon renamed* The Jack Paar Show*).*

and a prizewinner at that, for Braniff International, that was directed by Richard Lester and that probably did, as rumor had it, cost $100,000; it left me singing "Up, Up and Away TWA." There was a Benson and Hedges message, showing what seemed like scores of people inhaling deeply; it looked like nothing so much as a warning from the American Cancer Society. It is not funny when producers try to make furniture sexy and have it saying things like "pat our seats, pull our drawers . . ."

But most of the festival was pure entertainment and there's even more in the future. For next year the festival organizers are planning a 10-year retrospective, a showing of all 88 previous Clio-winners. These commercial classics include such gems as the Dreyfus Fund's "Lion in the Street," the dancing Old Gold cigarette packs, Gillette's "How Are You Fixed?", that enchanting Chinese baby who sat in its high chair trying to eat Jell-O with chopsticks, Muriel the sexy cigar singing "Come up and smoke me sometime" and, yes, fear not, Bert and Harry for Piels beer. I can hardly wait.

The alertness of See It Now *to large issues brought into focus by local events was demonstrated by this coverage in Knoxville, Tennessee, of sixteen agitators arrested for interfering with school desegregation in nearby Clinton, Tennessee. The disorder came with the Supreme Court civil rights decision of 1954.*

Walter Cronkite, a CBS reporter since 1950, was the narrator of The Twentieth Century, *a weekly series of documentaries on the history of our times which began in 1957. This one was the story of Winston Churchill, "Man of the Century." With him in a 1941 photograph are Mrs. Churchill and (next to her) Polish General Sikorski, reviewing Free Polish troops in England.*

J. Edgar Hoover appeared in "The F.B.I.," Don Whitehead's story of the Government police agency on The Twentieth Century.

A television playwright, Sam Bilkin, father of two small children, and concerned not only that his children were growing up with television as mentor and babysitter but with the decline of the Golden Age of TV drama, foresaw the influence of commercials in an article published in 1957 with the title "These Are My Children?"

When I read somewhere that television was living made easy for youngsters, that it was never too busy to talk, play, or share its work with them—I thought: How true, how true.

When I further read that the trouble was that parents excluded their children from adult activities, that the best solution was family viewing with critical discussions of the programs—I thought: How sensible, how intelligent, how civilized.

I rushed into the living room, for like all bewildered fathers of two absorbent offsprings I was naturally disturbed over the vexing problem of what television was doing to my children.

Patricia, 9, and Nancy, 8, were sprawled out on the couch, gazing hypnotically at a 17-inch screen that not only talked, played, shared—but made faces at them too.

"Girls," I said, "we shall all watch television together. As a family unit."

Nancy threw me a disgusted look.

Patricia said: "No baseball?"

"No baseball," I said, "We'll watch whatever you want to watch. Then we'll discuss the program."

"What's discuss?" Nancy asked.

"Discuss. Have a conversation."

"What's conversation?"

This historic TV image showed two former Presidents, Harry S. Truman and the late Herbert Hoover (behind eagle standard), sharing the platform with the newly elected Chief Executive.

The inauguration of the later President Eisenhower in 1953 was the first to be watched as well as heard by the entire nation, including these school children especially assembled for the event.

"Conversation. Have a discussion."

Patricia said: "Do we have to?"

"We don't *have* to. But it would be very nice if we did."

"Why?"

"That way we'd be a family unit."

"What's a family unit?" Nancy asked.

"Family unit. Us, as one."

"What's usasone?"

"Usasone," I said and frowned. "Now let's stop being a couple of wiseguys."

I turned the dial. *Strike It Rich* didn't seem to be the kind of show I wanted my kids to watch A cooking program came on, but Patricia said:

"Who ever wants to watch cooking?"

"Yes," Nancy said, "Who ever?"

"Okay," I said, "Change it to whatever you want."

Both girls went for the dial and naturally Patricia hauled off and socked Nancy, and naturally Nancy hauled off and socked Patricia, and naturally both of them hauled off and socked me for trying to keep them apart. They cried and I switched the channel.

"Okay," I said, "No more crying. Everybody sit down and watch the picture. It's about lions and tigers."

They watched for a moment, and then Nancy asked:

"What's the tiger doing?"

I said: "Looking for something to eat."

"Why?"

"Because he's hungry."

"For candy?"

"Don't be silly."

"I'm hungry for candy."

Wrestling was television's first love among professional sports, because it was easiest to cover with the equipment available in the early days. This photo made in the Fifties shows that many ardent fans were women. Viewers at home looked upon most of the matches as low comedy.

Baseball fans will drop a nostalgic tear over this 1956 photo when the Brooklyn Dodgers played in Ebbets Field. Manager Walter Alston and coach Billy Herman are playing host to Dizzy Dean, who was to broadcast the game on TV.

Peyton Place transported soap opera to prime evening time and transmitted the sexual escapades of small town people into TV gold. It also elevated pretty Mia Farrow to stardom.

"Just watch the picture."

They watched for still another moment, then Patricia asked: "What does a tiger eat?

"Flesh."

"No, they don't."

"Okay, they don't."

"Meat?"

"Yes. Meat."

"Like Nancy?"

"Yes. Like Nancy."

Patricia sank her teeth into Nancy's arm and I shot up out of the chair.

"Tigers wouldn't like Nancy," Patricia said. "She's sour."

As the sheriff of mythical Mayberry, Andy Griffith starred in the Andy Griffith Show *beginning in 1960. He confronts an unusual human problem in this scene.*

The Dick Van Dyke Show, *one of the more believable, better-written comedy series, started in 1961. Dick Van Dyke and Mary Tyler Moore starred.*

The phone rang. Nancy beat me to it.

"Hello! Breyer's calling!"

I grabbed the phone from her. It was my wife. "Hurry home," I said. "We're having a family unit."

"What's a family unit?" she asked.

"Family unit. Us, as one."

"What's usasone?"

"Usasone," I said and stopped. "Hurry home." I hung up and when I got back in the living room the picture was off in favor of a commercial.

"All right," I said, "Now what did you think of the picture?"

"Better buy Birdseye!" Patricia sang out.

"Look sharp! Feel sharp! Be sharp!" Nancy sang out.

"Stop it!" I said and turned off the set. "Now what kinds of programs do we like best?"

The broadcast of Arthur Miller's Death of a Salesman *in 1966 proved to be one of the most rewarding hours ever seen on the air. Lee J. Cobb (right) as Willy Loman, Mildred Dunnock as Linda Loman, George Segal (hand upraised) and James Farentino as sons Biff and Hap are seen above in a stirring scene in the 1967 repeat.*

"Snap! Pop! Crackle!"

"Mannnn—that's *coffee!*"

"Swing to Beechnut Chewing Gum!"

"Heyyyyy—get your Ballantine!"

"It's a Fo-o-o-o-orrrrdddd . . ."

"See the U.S.A.—in your Chev-ro-let . . ."

I suppose I screamed because Patricia and Nancy were suddenly bawling. I dashed into my room, slammed the door and hid behind the bed. Suddenly the full impact of what this meant conked me a one-two, and left me trembling. I—me—who was brought up on books, the love and respect for books, the magic and delight of reading—*I* am bringing up a couple of blonde-headed walking commercials. As kids we used to sing things like: "Yankee Doodle went to town . . ." My kids sing things like: "Winston, Winston—tastes good . . ." I shrank behind my bed, stared at the blank wall and asked myself two formidable questions:

1. Can it be that TV commercials are more absorbing than the programs themselves?
2. These are *my* children?

In the authors' opinion, television commercials provide a mathematical measure of the medium's influence superior to any listener surveys or rating system. An advertiser's willingness to invest huge sums in a few seconds of time on the air proves that he is usually repaid by sales of his product. It may be stated without exaggeration that in all probability a saturation campaign on television can sell anything—whether a product, a person, or an idea—that is not inordinately repulsive. As a hypothetical example, observers used to suggest that if the cigarette commercials appearing on the tube every few minutes, day after day and night after night, were replaced by anti-cigarette commercials, the smoking habit could be wiped out in a year.

Johnny Carson stepped into the shoes left vacant by Steve Allen and Jack Paar on the Tonight Show *in 1962 and scored with his own brand of humor. Here he exchanges a quip with the droll Buddy Hackett as his straightman Ed McMahon looks on.*

This suggestion was not lost upon public health authorities when cigarette smoking was statistically associated with lung cancer in the Fifties and the findings, extended to other respiratory and circulatory ailments as well, were confirmed in the Sixties. In 1968, TV stations that carried cigarette advertising were required to provide some degree of counterbalance by also carrying anti-smoking spots prepared by the Advertising Council for the American Cancer Society, American Heart Association, and National Tuberculosis Association. While the effectiveness of the campaign awaited the test of time, the tobacco companies acknowledged it by diversifying into other businesses—just in case.

Drama, original and unoriginal

In 1966 the *Hallmark Hall of Fame* began its 16th season on NBC, its productions consisting generally of adaptations such as Maxwell Anderson's *Barefoot in Athens* and Noel Coward's *Blithe Spirit*. But still another effort to revive original drama on TV was made with *ABC Stage 66*, which would become *ABC Stage 67* the following year. The idea behind the show was to attract the work of leading playwrights and composers who had not written for television before, and to cast their plays with major performers from other media. *CBS Playhouse*, also designed to bring original works to television, was launched the same year, joined in 1967 by *NBC Experiment in Television*. None of these produced anything especially memorable. The creative talent in drama simply had moved on to other fields, such as the Broadway or Off-Broadway stage and "adult" films, or if they remained with television, they worked on documentaries and entertainment specials. The year 1966 is better remembered for Arthur Miller's *Death of a Salesman* on CBS, or *The Battle for Asia*, a three-part report on NBC, or the direct coverage by NBC of the U.S. Senate hearings on the Vietnam war.

War and documentaries

The escalation of American involvement in Southeast Asia was a difficult story to report on TV, dangerous, complex because of its extraordinary mix of military, political, and moral aspects. All the networks with their camera crews did an excellent job both in commentary and in field reporting. Morley Safer of CBS

won half a dozen awards for the latter; it was plain to every viewer that television reporters were right where the mortar shells were flying. The impact could be measured by rising resistance to the war at home; by burning of draft cards, the formation of a New Left political movement, open rebellion on college campuses, the entry of Senator Eugene F. McCarthy and the reentry of Senator Robert Kennedy into a campaign for the Democratic nomination, and the withdrawal of President Johnson from renomination in 1968.

An ambitious program measuring the new stature of the television documentary was *Africa,* presented in color by ABC in four hours of prime time on September 10, 1967. It was hailed by critics as an "event" in itself, combining the news resources of the network with comment by leading experts. *Africa* went on to win the George Polk award, and to become a series of hour-long telecasts and films for schools. ABC also won an Emmy award for its documentary on Westminster Abbey, and much praise for *Ivan Ivanovich,* an intimate look at the daily life of a Soviet family.

Among CBS news specials in 1967 was a modestly presented conversation between Eric Severeid and longshoreman-philosopher Eric Hoffer. It drew so much mail and created so much comment that the tapes were re-run a couple of weeks later. The episode upset many theories about television; it showed that stimulating ideas when presented in a natural, non-stagy way could capture an audience as thoroughly as more elaborate productions.

Memorable documentaries on NBC included *Khrushchev in Exile,* and *Bravo Picasso* which utilized the satellite to telecast in color the story of the famous painter's life, climaxed by the sale of his painting, *Femme Couchée Lisant,* for $105,000 in a three-nation television auction. Among memorable entertainments were (on CBS) *Mark Twain Tonight* with Hal Holbrook, which many veteran viewers ranked as the most remarkable single performance ever seen on the tube. It was, of course, a presentation of a routine which Mr. Holbrook had perfected in years of touring as an impersonator of Mark Twain, not likely to be duplicated by any studio product.

1967 marked TV's coming of age in another way: it was now old enough for nostalgia and reprise. Sid Caesar, Imogene Coca, Carl Reiner, and Howard Morris were brought together for one night to recapture the bounce and charm of their old *Show of Shows.* The habit of late-night listening was firmly implanted when *The Joey Bishop Show* made its debut on ABC in competition with NBC's *Tonight Show* with Johnny Carson. The following year the *Merv Griffin Show* was moved up from daytime to nighttime on CBS, completing the threesome of talkers, and in 1969 Dick Cavett joined the club as a summer replacement on ABC.

Leading shows of 1968–1969

The decade of the Sixties is not yet ended as this is written. The last complete season, September 1968 to March 1969, placed the 40 leading shows as follows, according to the Nielsen index. (The A. C. Nielsen Company defined its "average audience rating" as the number of TV households tuned to a program during the average minute as a percent of total U.S. TV households—an estimate rather than a precise mathematical value.)

1.	Rowan & Martin	31.3 NBC	21.	Dragnet	21.4 NBC
2.	Gomer Pyle	27.2 CBS		Ed Sullivan	21.4 CBS
3.	Bonanza	26.9 NBC		Walt Disney	21.4 NBC
4.	Mayberry RFD	25.9 CBS	24.	Carol Burnett	21.2 CBS
5.	Family Affair	25.4 CBS		Smothers Brothers	21.2 CBS
6.	Julia	25.1 NBC	26.	Jackie Gleason	21.1 CBS
7.	Gunsmoke	24.8 CBS	27.	Monday Movie	20.8 NBC
8.	Dean Martin	24.0 NBC	28.	I Dream of Jeannie	20.6 NBC
9.	Here's Lucy	23.6 CBS	29.	Lawrence Welk	20.5 ABC
	Red Skelton	23.6 CBS	30.	Doris Day	20.4 CBS
11.	Beverly Hillbillies	23.4 CBS		Thursday Movie	20.4 CBS
	Mission: Impossible	23.4 CBS	32.	Friday Movie	20.3 CBS
13.	Bewitched	23.3 ABC	33.	Lancer	20.2 CBS
14.	My Three Sons	22.5 CBS		Tuesday Movie	20.2 NBC
	Glen Campbell	22.5 CBS	35.	Mod Squad	20.0 ABC
16.	The FBI	22.4 ABC		Petticoat Junction	20.0 CBS
17.	Ironside	22.1 NBC		Saturday Movie	20.0 NBC
18.	The Virginian	21.8 NBC	38.	Good Guys	19.8 CBS
19.	Green Acres	21.6 CBS		Hogan's Heroes	19.8 CBS
20.	Daniel Boone	21.5 NBC		Mothers-in-Law	19.8 NBC

Joan Baez, one of the best known singers of folk music appeared infrequently. Here she appears in a series called "The Creative Person," for NET, giving expression to her political opinions as well as her music.

The above were regular weekly shows. The big "one-shot" specials during the same season ranked like this:

1.	Bob Hope Christmas Show, Jan. 16	38.5	NBC
2.	Superbowl (pro football championship), Jan. 12	36.0	NBC
3.	Bob Hope Show, Nov. 6	35.7	NBC
4.	Bob Hope Show, Dec. 19	35.5	NBC
5.	Bob Hope Show, Feb. 17	34.9	NBC
6.	Rose Bowl (college (football), Jan. 1)	33.5	NBC
7.	Singer Presents Elvis (Presley), Dec. 3	32.0	NBC
8.	Heidi, Nov. 17	31.8	NBC
9.	Jack Benny's Birthday Special, Feb. 17	30.4	NBC
10.	Bob Hope Show, Oct. 14	30.0	NBC

Some of the names on this list (Lucy, Red Skelton, Jackie Gleason, Ed Sullivan) had been on similar lists since the Forties or early Fifties. Others (*Gunsmoke,* Dean Martin, *Dragnet,* Lawrence Welk) represented types of shows that had not changed materially over the years. With very few exceptions (Smothers Brothers, Rowan and Martin, Carol Burnett, for example) the list would lead one to the conclusion that television had not in its nearly thirty years contributed anything original to the entertainment art. That conclusion would be substantially correct. Television simply borrowed the talents and ideas of vaudeville, night clubs, the musical stage, radio, and films . . . multiplied the audiences by a factor of millions . . . consumed new material at profligate speed . . . and settled down to production of machine-made "comedy" and

The unique Beatles, quartet of mad music-makers, took the country by storm when they first appeared in the U. S. in 1964, on the Ed Sullivan Show.

"drama" or "variety" in well-worn grooves as suggested by the show titles. Even the leading specials were six-tenths Bob Hope and Jack Benny *(Hope and Benny?)* and two-tenths football. Among the few foundations was the assigning of black actors to sympathetic starrinng roles *(Julia, Mod Squad)* without, however, getting them fictionally involved in racial issues.

Less than one month after the above lists were compiled, the high-rated *Smothers Brothers Comedy Hour* was abruptly canceled by CBS, allegedly for failing to submit a topical, satirical program for advance review. According to Tom and Dick Smothers, the real issue was cencorship—not by the Government, but by the industry itself, fearful of treading on Establishment toes. The trouble had been brewing for some time over network editing of "irreverent" or "offensive" material out of the show. In defending its action, CBS seemed to set a double standard: news coverage and documentaries were the place "to provide a forum for dissident and anti-Establishment views," but *entertainment* programs were not. In Washington, a Senate subcommittee on communications headed by Senator John Pastore (Dem., R.I.) found grist for its mill in the question of "Who controls TV?"

The truly great achievements of the medium thus do not appear in Nielsen rating lists or in capital letters on the networks' profit-and-loss reports. They appear in the history of the life of the people, and the year 1968 wrote these achievements in a large, ungainly scrawl.

The problem of violence

It was a year of violence gone beyond all reason, and of a public "backlash" to violence that would be tested in a national election. The assassination of Martin Luther King by a sniper during a civil rights campaign in Memphis, Tennessee (with some evidence of a hired assassin) plunged the entire nation, white as well as black, into mourning and spiritual depression. The spectacle of thousands upon thousands of people in Atlanta, Georgia, marching in grim silence to King's funeral, shown without interruption on everyone's television screen, was unquestionably one of the most moving gestures of respect and somber regret ever paid to a person not a high government official. The rioting that followed, and the humiliating failure of the Poor People's March on Washington that

After his break with Jerry Lewis, Dean Martin (at left, with Frank Sinatra) showed that he was a fine performer on his own and reached his peak with the Dean Martin Show *in 1965.*

King had planned but could not carry out—all fully reported on TV—dramatized the magnitude of the loss of leadership for orderly resolution of America's racial problems.

When, within a few weeks, a Jordanian Arab nationalist named Sirhan Sirhan shot U. S. Senator Robert Kennedy to death at a political rally, the nation woke up to the realization that violence had become a contagious disease. The President appointed a Commission on Violence, a gun-control law was introduced in Congress —and television felt the hot breath of angered criticism. As early as 1962, a report to a Senate sub-committee on juvenile delinquency had cited research evidence indicating that TV entertainment programs were indoctrinating children with an acceptance of murder and mayhem. At that time Senator Abraham Ribicoff of Connecticut had said, "More detailed research is necessary before we can say for sure whether beatings, robberies, and murders which darken the television screen are harmful to young people." But in the year of horror, 1968, people were ready to conclude that the research was in.

Since 1960, while the nation's population grew 10 per cent, the crime rate had risen 86 per cent. Furthermore, the fastest growth in crime statistics had occurred among the youth who had grown up with TV sets as their baby-sitters. The National Association for Better Broadcasting estimated that the average child between ages 5 and 15 would see more than 13,000 persons violently destroyed on TV in the guise of entertainment, and added:

> Most are gunned down, but fire, rape, poison, acid, spiders, snakes, crocodiles, pitchforks, knives, time bombs, live steam, poison gas, hypodermic needles, and an assortment of heavy blunt instruments are all used to add spice and variety and thrills to the spectacle of death.

The three network presidents, Dr. Frank Stanton of CBS, Julian Goodman of NBC, and Leonard H. Goldenson of ABC hastened to issue directives calling for the toning down of violent scenes in 1969 programming. Showings of certain motion pictures, *Blackboard Jungle* and *Prescription: Murder,* were cancelled, as were episodes in various series ranging from routine Western gunplay to a gang war in *The Flying Nun.* Producers of Saturday morning cartoons for children rushed to sanitize the horror out of them, too.

Children running wild

Even if these efforts were sincere, they would be difficult to enforce short of government censorship. In the light of events, they were a thimbleful of water cast upon a forest fire. During 1968 and '69, the young generation that had grown up with TV seemed to run amok. In Chicago a Yippie (Youth for Political Action) demonstration for Senator "Gene" McCarthy during the Democratic National Convention turned into a fierce street battle with club-swinging, gas-throwing police. Gorily and some thought cynically displayed in full on home screens, this unwholesome spectacle thoroughly shocked the American public. Reactions to it made a travesty of the nominating process at the convention, raised such issues as "police brutality" and "law and order" in the ensuing campaign, and unquestionably cost Vice President Hubert H. Humphrey the presidency in a close election.

Young students of a similar violent turn made a shambles of another Establishment bastion—the great liberal arts university. A kind of frenzy swept from the Berkeley campus of the University of California to Columbia, Harvard, Yale, and scores of others (including Negro colleges) as students shouted "Revolution!" in the name of Vietnam peace and freer admission policies for the black minority. They followed a suspiciously set pattern: "non-negotiable" demands, provocations, occupied buildings, the holding of deans as hostages, fights with police, and wild vandalism. Again TV focused its crisis eye on trouble; thus a view of militant black students bearing rifles as they occupied a Cornell building looked to all the world like civil war.

The merits of the opposing sides do not concern the television historian, but these confrontations established the *power potential* of the medium at an undreamed of level. The acts of a relatively few icon-smashers, when mega-magnified by 57 million living-room tubes, could now shake society to its most time-tested foundations. Demonstrators deliberately played to the TV cameras, almost ignoring the ostensible targets—at the scene such as convention delegates or college negotiators. In this sense the disturbances were staged, a half-truth rather than indisputable fact. They echoed the show-business morality revealed by rigged quizes a decade earlier—the idea than an effective image matters more than a sober assessment of what is, or is not, true.

To thoughtful persons, the prospects for future manipulation of events were frightening. In the end, the "Dump the Hump" brawl in Chicago not only split and defeated the Democratic Party, but very nearly precipitated a constitutional crisis—had "backlash" candidate George Wallace received enough electoral votes to throw the choice of a president into Congress. Contemplating the future of the nation's educational system with responsibility in tatters, one could only shudder.

TV in the future

In the Sixties television, the medium, emerged as the message of modern civilization. In 1968 the Republican nominee for president, Richard M. Nixon, the same who had exhausted himself in futile personal barnstorming around the nation in 1960, announced that his entire campaign would stand or fall on television appearances. The costs, mounting to the millions of dollars, meant the American presidency now might be beyond the reach of any man lacking (a) a personal fortune or the financial support of wealthy individuals, and (b) an attractive television demeanor. (Attractiveness had already projected two California actors on to the national scene, U. S. Senator George Murphy and state Governor Ronald Reagan, both Republican Conservatives.)

To the older generation, the world of the late Sixties seemed topsy-turvy, in the throes of a revolution without defined objectives. To the younger generation, the revolt meant a rejection of middle-class values extolled daily on the television screen, and the embracing of anarchistic values ranging from LSD to underground cinema to love-ins. It was natural to blame television, at least in part, for the crumbling of a society and the menace to its Establishment. But others could insist that television simply "told it the way it was," reflecting modern attitudes even in the very childishness of most TV fiction. There was no question, as the Seventies approached, that television would both shape and be shaped by a strange new world in the making.

On New Year's Day, 1952, Edward R. Murrow uttered a prophetic comment on television's destiny. He said:

> This instrument can teach, it can illuminate, it can even inspire, but only if human beings are willing to use it to those ends. Otherwise it is only wires and lights in a box.

By special television coverage, millions around the world saw astronaut Edwin Aldrin, Jr. walk on the surface of the moon. The lunar landing took place July 20, 1969. In the foreground are footprints of Aldrin and astronaut Neil Armstrong. Michael Collins remained in the Command Module. The astronauts successfully splashed down in the Pacific Ocean on July 24 and recovery was made by the U.S.S. Horne. All phases of this spectacular event were televised.

Index

208

IRVING SETTEL

Irving Settel has been associated with broadcasting for many years, co-producing "Where Have You Been?" for the NBC Radio Network, and creating "Who's The Boss?" for ABC Television and "Who Pays?" for NBC-TV. He is the author of eighteen books including HOW TO WRITE TELEVISION COMEDY, TOP TV SHOWS OF THE YEAR, THE BEST OF ARMSTRONG CIRCLE THEATRE and the definitive TELEVISION ADVERTISING AND PRODUCTION HANDBOOK. Mr. Settel is Director of the Educational Technology Department at Pace College and an Associate Professor of Marketing.

WILLIAM LAAS

William Laas is the author, co-author, or principal editor of eighteen previous books on a wide range of factual subjects. He has also been executive editor of *Holiday, Magazine of the Year,* and *Ford Times,* as well as a contributor to *McCall's, This Week, Esquire, The New York Times Magazine, Saturday Evening Post,* and other national publications. As a young newspaper writer and syndicate editor in New York, he was an early observer and chronicler of television's infancy as a medium of communication.

Among Mr. Laas's recent books have been *The Feel of Road, Women! Business Needs You, The Water In Your Life, Crossroads of the World —The Story of Times Square, Cuisines of the Eastern World,* and *Guide for Young Homemakers.*